Janette Laidlaw

D1545226

35

THE SWEET CRY OF HOUNDS

DAN RUSSEL THE FOX

THE SWEET CRY OF HOUNDS

BY

E. Œ. SOMERVILLE

AND

MARTIN ROSS

Authors of
'The Smile and the Tear'
'Some Experiences of an Irish R.M.'
&c., &c.

ILLUSTRATED BY

E. Œ. S.

BOSTON AND NEW YORK
HOUGHTON MIFFLIN COMPANY
1937

PRINTED IN GREAT BRITAIN

CONTENTS

ILLUSTRATIONS

PLATES

IN THE TEXT

vii

REYNARD THE FOX

(Traditional Irish)

The first day of spring in the year ninety-three,
The first recreation was in this country,
The King's county gentlemen o'er hills, dales and rocks,
They rode out so jovially in search of a fox.

Chorus

Tally-ho! Hark away! Tally-ho! Hark away!
Tally-ho! Hark away, me boys! Away! Hark away!

When Reynard was started he faced Tullamore,
Arklow and Wicklow along the seashore.
We kept his brush in view every yard of the way,
And he straight took his course thro' the streets of Roscrea.

Chorus

But Reynard, sly Reynard, lay hid there that night,
And they swore they would watch him until the daylight;
Early next morning the woods they did resound
With the echo of horns and the sweet cry of hounds.

Chorus

When Reynard was started he faced to the hollow;
Where none but the hounds and the footmen could follow
The gentlemen cried 'watch him, watch him, what shall we do,
If the rocks do not stop him he will cross Killaloe!'

Chorus

ix

THE SWEET CRY OF HOUNDS

When Reynard was taken, his wishes to fulfil,
He called for ink and paper and pen to write his will;
And what he made mention of they found it no *blank*,
For he gave them a *check* on the National *Bank*!

Chorus

To you, Mr. Casey, I give my whole estate;
And to you, young O'Brien, my money and my plate;
And I give to you, Sir Francis, my whip, spurs, and cap,
For you crossed walls and ditches and ne'er looked for a gap!

Chorus

Tally-ho! Hark away! Tally-ho! Hark away!
Tally-ho! Hark away, me boys! Away! Hark away!

I

COMMENCING MASTER

SO many people have thought about Hunting, and have thought so much, and have recorded their thoughts so voluminously, that it would seem that any further reflections should remain unrecorded.

Yet the angle at which one approaches the subject is essentially personal, and there may always be a facet that might shine if a light that is sympathetic should chance to illuminate it.

Take, for example, the trepidations of the Youth—or, in these days, one may say also the Maiden—who is ' commencing Master '. Trepidation is indeed a word that is quite inadequate to convey an idea of the nerve-strain that can afflict a new-born M.F.H. He has possibly felt his way through the preliminaries, the letters to and from the Committee, the setting-forth of his qualifications, with some anxiety, but though the roses may not have blossomed on his path all the way, the end has been success. He has had the summer months in which to find his footing in the Kennels. The kind hounds know him—or pretend they do, being accomplished in cajolery—he is pretty sure that he knows them and can correctly apply their names. He has indeed given more honest work to the task than ever his schooldays knew in the matter of Dates and Dynasties. The road-work has been instructive in giving him insight into their characters. Soon he begins to believe that he can face the responsibilities of his lofty position. He has not yet realized how truly Shakespeare spoke when he remarked ' uneasy lies the head that wears a velvet cap ' (or words to that effect). He looks forward to the Cubbing with enjoyment and complacency, and has no fear of criticism. The opinions of Rat-catchers at dawn are negligible ; it is the Opening Day of the season, when the grave and reverent seniors of the Hunt have to be met, that is the ordeal that matters.

I am thinking of a small Irish Hunt, and even though nothing in Ireland is quite what it is elsewhere, I believe its type will be recognized when I say that it was the sort of pack whose Master is either a very young beginner, or a very ancient fossil, a survival from prehistoric times. In this particular case the Master was very young, and was re-creating a Pack that, with the demise of a fossil, had passed into oblivion ; no easy task, since there were still some survivors of the prehistoric period, who had canonized the fossil and distrusted youth.

But if the First Day of the Season has its anxieties, it has, for the young Master, also its consolations. To ride forth on the best horse in the stable, up on his toes, polished and proud, as aware of the greatness of the occasion as his rider. To adore the decorous gaiety of the hounds, as they flow and ripple along the road before him. To note the brilliance of his Whip's new scarlet coat, and to reflect that his own is equally beautiful ; these are nerve-tonics that help him to forget the fear of the Elder Statesmen, all charged to the muzzle with criticism though they surely are, while he can look forward with confidence to the friendly crowd of foot-people, whose discussion of all things, Horses, Hounds, and Riders, is unintermittent as the buzz of a hard-working hive.

I have known a temperamental budding M.F.H., normally of a good courage, who, on the morning of his opening meet, sat, pale and gloomy, in total silence, at the breakfast-table, refusing to eat or drink. A remarkably different being from the crimson-faced youth who, not many hours later, was handling his first November fox, and shouting— (addressing in fancy, the absent uncle who had disparaged his capacity)—' Now ! Who says I don't know my damned job ! '

A reasonable measure of success, and a few triumphs,

3

is usually sufficient for a beginning Master to acquire the aura of grudged prestige that is the award of a fault-finding Field. For it must be conceded that the generality of

'ALL CHARGED TO THE MUZZLE WITH CRITICISM'

Fields find fault. After all, how else can they pass the time during a long draw of—say—a wide woodland covert ? The sort of covert in which hounds are lost as finally and irrevocably as in death. Over, over, over, they go. The Huntsman follows them. The Whip gallops into what might be the next world. Silence falls

'NOW! WHO SAYS I DON'T KNOW MY DAMNED JOB!'

The Field, penned, probably, in a fastness as remote from the covert as the ingenuity of the Field master can find, feel, as the song says, that it may be for years and it

5

may be for ever before they see Hounds again, and fall morosely to censure and cigarettes. Yet, on the whole, assuming the youth and want of experience of the Master who carries the horn, it is an open question that the exiled Field are not in a more fortunate position than he, little as they may think it.

Of such a covert as I have postulated, let me take as an example an Irish wood that I know well. Such an ancient forest of hollies and stunted oaks as Southern Ireland can provide as a sanctuary for foxes, and badgers, and rabbits ; with narrow rides, dedicated to woodcock shooters rather than to foxhunters, and muddy cattle-tracks, webbed about with briars, paths that have the peculiar gift of leading nowhere, unless, circuitously, to the spot in a main ride whence they started. It is such a wood as would make the fortune of a fairy-tale. Once involved in its depths the sense of direction is lost. Rides and cattle-tracks combine into a maze, and the points of the compass are swallowed up in darkness and mystery.

Let us try and visualize the young Master, who has accepted the imaginative assurances of the Earth-stopper that the wood is hopping with foxes, and has committed himself, with the hounds, to its depths. He moves slowly along what appears to be the central ride, while, to encourage and stimulate the unseen hounds, he utters uncertain sounds that are half-strangled at birth by self-consciousness. He attempts to touch the horn, and tells himself, after having achieved one or two brief explosive noises, that if he blew till he burst a blood-vessel he would never get a decent note out of it, and if he did, the hounds wouldn't give a curse for it. His new velvet cap is switched and lashed by the low branches, his new scarlet coat is splashed with inky mud from the sloughs which are frequent incidents in such a wood, and from which only the superior wisdom of his horse saves him, since the mischievous woodland spirits will surely have masked them with dead leaves in order to betray invaders.

He plods on, steering an uncertain course by the occasional sight of a hound bustling through the undergrowth, and with further assistance from squeals from some of the young entry, indicating enjoyable encounters with rabbits.

He is blind to the sudden glimpses of beauty that the wood can offer, when a long glade is lit by a gleam of sun, and at its farther end, beyond its yellow sedge, and orange bracken, and grey boulders, a lovely vision of blue hills is bestowed.

For him is only conviction of failure. He is certain of a black succession of mutually opposed disasters. That there isn't a fox in the wood. That all the foxes are stopped in. That the Field will head the fox when he breaks. That the Whip is on the wrong side of the covert, but (nevertheless) *he* will go away with the hounds and a fox,

2

while he—the miserable Master—will spend the rest of the day trying to find the way out.

And then, sometimes, the Wheel of Fortune will turn, and something low and swift will glide across his path, and the young Master will forget himself and all things earthly, as he cheers his hounds to their fox, and goes crashing out of covert at their sterns.

I I

HOUNDS

IT may be asserted without much fear of contradiction, that for the M.F.H. who is born rather than made, the chief and deepest interest that the position can afford is to be found in the Kennels.

I will assume that the Beginner has been appointed to a small and quite unfashionable pack, and—other things being equal—let it be in Southern Ireland that he, as so many have done, first begins to learn his trade. What is described as ' Spit-and-Polish ' may, in such an establishment, be wanting, but the root of the matter is there, and efficiency will not be found lacking.

Twenty-two couple—let us say—of foxhounds offer forty-four individual psychological problems to the person who realizes his privileges. Let us consider the Commencing Master at the opening of his career, in or about the month of May, paying his first visit to the Kennels. With his kennel-huntsman (who is also his Whip) he stands in the middle of a moving carpet of black and white and tan, that resolves itself ceaselessly into fresh patterns, and in the deep of an anxious heart he feels that for him the patterns will never resolve themselves into individuals. Perhaps, he thinks, if he could only remember her name, he might be able to apply it correctly to that lovely bitch with the tan head, who is exemplifying for him Robert Louis Stevenson's definition—' that carneying mass of affectation, the female dog '—but it seems unlikely.

The kennel-man has filled the deep pockets of his Master's snowy new kennel-coat with broken biscuit. The Master doesn't know it, but the hounds do. The glowing faces are all turned towards him. The beaming eyes are all seeking his eye, each resolved to make contact with his spirit, to engross his attention, to persuade him that he, Pillager, or she, Madrigal, is alone worthy of those hidden hoards. All the pack, dogs and bitches, are assembled in one yard, and now begins that detailed biography of each of them which is, or should be, charged with equal interest for narrator and listener. Recitals such as these are limited only by one of the great primary facts of life, such as feeding-time for the Hounds, or the same for their guardian—(the meals of the Master are of secondary importance).

The young Master listens attentively—we may assume that he is a conscientious young Master—and tries to connect such attributes as a black face and a tendency to dwell on the line, with the name of 'Tarquin' or 'Reckless', while he responds suitably to the Biographer's demand for appreciation. No mother, no nurse, however devoted, can be as avid of praise of her nurselings, as is the kennel-huntsman who is parading his pack. Shoulders, neck, bone, back, feet, the listener must not fail of admiration, as intelligent as he can make it, for some, if not all of these points.

'And now, Master, you'll see them fed?'

It is posed as an inquiry, but it is more than a command ; it expresses a gratifying conviction that the new Master's heart is in the right place.

'That's a lovely pudden',' the leading artist says, critically surveying his handiwork, as his satellite, the sub-chef, deposits the blocks of oatmeal porridge in the feeding-trough, and proceeds to mash and distribute the 'pudden'' with an instrument that suggests a gridiron which has sprouted and gone to seed in a long stem. The young Master agrees. If he is wise he doesn't even sniff when a bucket of full-flavoured soup, enriched with hideous and mysterious fragments, is slopped over the porridge. Then he watches the expert process of 'drawing' the hounds by name for their meal. They have been put back into the kennel ; the arbiter stands at the narrowly opened door, his crop, with the thong doubled back, in his hand, summoning each hound by name, tapping him or her gently with his crop, watching approvingly as the chosen one squeezes through the narrow opening and darts to the trough to gobble at full speed.

Feeding hounds is, as has been said, an expert process. The order of the guests is nicely determined by their appetite and capacity. The young and shy feeders come first, and

ONE PATHETIC OUTCAST

in the comparative leisure that is granted to them, choose their places at the trough. One by one the rest of the pack, who have waited in agony of suspense, join the banquet. They force their jealous way between those who have been given so unfair a start, leaping over the stubborn backs of the first comers who will not yield space, distracted by fear lest all the best bits are gone. As often as not there is one pathetic outcast, whose greed and speed are such that only at what must feel like the eleventh hour, the door is flung wide, and the poor glutton can make up for the past moments of despair.

It has chanced to me, during a fortnight's holiday of my Huntsman, to act as his representative, and to arbitrate at the daily dinner-party. Only an amateur as inexperienced as I can realize with what anxiety I awaited, on his return, the verdict of the Chief Butler. He surveyed each hound slowly and with a searching eye. Then he pronounced these words :

' You fed 'em very nice, Master. Very nice indeed ! '

I took the bouquet, I hope, sedately, but my heart—as a poet has said—my heart was like a singing-bird.

The meal disposed of, follows ' Walking-out ', a ceremony that resembles some high ecclesiastical rite. Led by what might seem a white-robed priest, the hounds follow in the calm of repletion, with another white-robed ministrant bringing up the rear. Docile they move along the accustomed way, toddling submissively, with waving sterns, behind the High-priest. Many times, in a green pasture-field, high above a bland summer sea, I have enjoyed the pastoral scene ; the older hounds gravely rolling, gravely eating grass, the young ones chasing each other in circles that have an illicit tendency to widen, if the eye of authority is for

13

an instant closed. White figures, with the blue sea behind them, green grass, and the gay-coloured hounds playing on it in sunlight—it is a picture that memory holds fast.

There are few things more remarkable than the power of hounds to learn and remember their names. It must

WALKING-OUT

often chance that, in a draft, a hound arrives with a name that is already in use in the pack to which he has come. Yet the alternative name is learned and accepted with a readiness not always achieved by man or woman in like case. I bethink me of an occasion when a bitch named Tanzy was imported, in a draft, into a pack where was

14

another bitch named Fancy. Slight though was the differ-
ence in sound, neither of the ladies ever showed the least
uncertainty as to which was summoned, each knew and
responded to her respective name.

The arrival of a draft is a time of anxiety for a kennel-
huntsman. The new-comers may at first be kept separate,
but sooner or later they have to take their places in the
pack, and however much they may have 'walked out'
together, or, under the eye of authority, been included in
the family party by day, it is at night that the trouble ever
comes. There was a case of three dog-hounds being left to
sleep with the others of their sex, after what seemed sufficient
introduction. That night, unseen and unheard, hatred was
fulfilled in tragedy.

In the morning the kennel-man made a terse report.

' They have the strangers ate, Master. There was nothing
only their feet before me when I went in to them to-day.'

The need to introduce fresh blood makes an occasional
draft advisable, but almost the chief of the interests in running a pack of hounds is that of keeping up its numbers
by breeding from its known and trusted members. That
this procedure is often beset with disappointments is but too
true, but there is great and solid satisfaction in receiving
from ' walk ' a batch of healthy home-bred puppies, and in
seeing them eventually enter and do credit to their parents,
as well as to the judgement that decreed their parentage.

But it is with the arrival of the young entry that the real cares and anxieties of kennel management begin. Heartbreaking losses will, almost inevitably, have been reported from those homes to which the babies were entrusted. Sad letters from kind women who have to report that all their

AN OLD AND TRUSTED MEMBER

care and affection have been defeated by accident or illness, more often the latter. And after the safe arrival of a batch of blooming puppies at the kennels, Distemper, or that even more deadly disease, known as ' Yellows ', will fall out of a clear sky, and it is almost invariably the best of the young entry that are the victims.

16

Many are the panaceas and treatments. Probably most kennels have their own methods, but it may be suggested that coffee, as a preventive in times of infection, is not very generally known. It is at once a tonic and a germ-killer, and I have known a case of distemper in which a young hound, at the point of death, was saved by having a breakfast-cupful of strong coffee poured down his throat. Its special merit, however, is as a safeguard. Even if at first it is resented, if not abhorred, it can be made attractive to the most disapproving puppy by the improbable method of adding to the potion scraps of meat or fried fish, the result justifying Othello's complaint—'that we can call these delicate creatures ours, but not their appetites'!

III

HUNTING-HORSES

NOT the least agreeable of the duties that may or —as I think—ought to be involved in keeping hounds, is that of getting Horses and Hounds fit by Road-work. There is restfulness in the knowledge that there are no implacable time-tables, such as ordain meets, to be observed. It is a matter between oneself and one's conscience, and is regardless of the outside world.

One wakes easily in the pale summer dawn. An early cock challenges. One looks out of the window to vet. the weather, and hears—if one's bedroom is properly situated— the clank of a bucket in the stableyard, and the soft thunder of horses' feet stamping for the *petit déjeuner* that is all they are going to get. Then, having foregone all refinements of toilet, and, possibly, swallowed an amateur cup of tea, how enlivening to go out into the delicious early air, and, as one climbs into the saddle, to hear the hounds' morning hymn ! No one has told them that they are going out, but they have felt it long before it became a certainty with the arrival of their head-nurse and nursery-maid, clad in their shabbiest old scarlet coats. The waiting pack, shouting their rapture, come hustling out of the kennels and on to the road where the horses are waiting for them. Little Bridget, the grey mare, lays back her ears and pretends that she will devour that over-indulged old bitch, Rachel, who stands up on her hindlegs and puts her feet on Bridget's shoulder, baring her battered front teeth in a grin of adoration to Bridget's rider. Follows the peaceful jogging along the empty roads through the green scented summer country ; not a motor, not a man to be met or seen, only sleepy cows standing knee-high in dewy grass, and now and then a donkey rolling on the dusty road, or feeding in what in Ireland is known as ' the long meadow ' by the roadside. Fifteen or twenty miles at a ' Hounds-jog ' can give an appetite for breakfast, and horses, hounds and men come home happy and know that they have earned it.

These early morning heart-to-heart hours with hounds and horses are a sure way to that fellowship with them that is as pleasant a thing as life can give. Hounds are, to be sure, on a rather different basis from horses—that deep plane of mutual love and understanding on which, in secret, dogs and their owners can move, cannot, I think, be said to exist for horses. Yet there can also be a very intimate relationship between horse and rider, and when, in this connexion, horse is said, hunter should specially be understood.

If this intimacy is to endure and prosper, it should be entered into from the start. It should be, for the rider, love at first sight, an emotion beyond and above that which is inspired by the usual conventions of conformation, it must be a sudden passion that transcends the sordid consideration of price. I have myself experienced it many times, but never more masterfully than when I first met a small, dark grey, four-year-old mare, who has already been alluded to as Bridget.

This is not the first time that she has been mentioned in print, but to discuss hunting-horses and to omit mention of Bridget would be a disloyalty of which I am incapable.

Our first meeting was on a road near her owner's farm, at a bridge that spans a lovely creek, where the fierce Atlantic slides inland, tame as a canal. Bridget had jumped her way to freedom, but had just submitted to capture at her owner's hands, and I was invited to look at her. She was not quite fifteen hands two inches ; she had an erect mane, like a snowy quickset hedge, and a tail like a heavy white petticoat. She was rough and half-starved. But these were superficials—

Skin-deep, and valued at a pin is beauty such as Venus owns,
Her beauty is beneath the skin, and lies in layers on her bones.

20

Similarly, in the things that matter, Bridget could defy criticism.

I looked at her cross face. She put back her ears and snapped at me, but I understood her to say that she disliked John Connolly and I might do for a change

'SHE'S AS LOOSE AS A HARE,' SAID JOHN CONNOLLY

'She's as loose as a hare,' said John Connolly. 'She's too braichy for me. No fence'll stop her.'

It was an attractive quality, and the first tentacles that reach out towards a deal were delicately extended.

The next phase in the affair was a visit from Mr. Connolly, ostensibly to announce that a fox was parading his land every night and killing his wife's fowl. But he was riding the mare, and dismounting, he proceeded to engage me in conversation on general topics. The pursuance of the deal was indicated. It wore on in the accustomed way, but it ended as I had known from the first it would end, and once more love at first sight was justified.

There is, perhaps, no form of horse-dealing more interesting—if precarious—than buying a two-year-old on its breeding, with the hope that this may be relied on. Heredity can be misleading, but the risk is a sporting and enjoyable one. Let me tell of such an experience.

A couple of well-bred two-year-old colts had been ' harboured '—as ' warrantable ' stags are marked down—at a distance that involved not only a train journey, but also a long run in a car, and, when the rail had to be exchanged for the road, rain had begun to fall, determinately, even with enthusiasm. With equal determination, but without enthusiasm, I, with my counsellor in stable-matters, without whom no purchase is possible, entered the waiting car.

The first interview took place at a farm, whose only approach was by a lane in which fundamental rocks just showed their angular snouts above a sea of mud. The hireling Ford contemplated this for an instant, and refused. We proceeded under umbrellas on foot and by field. Finally a tall young creature, wet and shining, black and thin, was cornered in a field. Cottage and Crackenthorpe, Hermit, Perdita, Tracery, Princes and Princesses in the horses' Almanach de Gotha, were concerned in his pedigree.

'Better blood there's not in Ireland,' said his owner dispassionately.

His appearance suggested a cross between an eel and a

THROUGH THE VEILS OF RAIN

toast-rack, but, even through the veils of rain, one saw the great flat knees, the let-down jumping hindquarters, the well-balanced proportions of the slender immature frame, and the proud head, held high, with wild eyes that stared, horrified, at the umbrellas.

My counsellor was at my elbow. 'We shouldn't leave him after us,' he murmured in my ear, while the owner lashed the plunging colt round in a circle on the end of a rope

The conclusion of the deal was arrived at in a dark little den of indescribable uncleanness. Such a place as ought by all the canons of stable management to check growth and undermine health. But I bought the colt, subject to a vet., and he is now winning prizes at Hunter-Shows on the farther side of the Atlantic.

Thus far the expedition had justified itself ; we had tasted blood—and bought it !—and the rain, though by this time descending in torrents, was but an incident. For some fifteen miles we churned on through the sticky lime-stone mud of North Cork. I had fallen into profound meditation on the future of the black colt, when the car stopped with a jerk, and turned aside into a wide, grass-grown, deeply rutted track, that had once been a high road. Slowly we moved along it, groping our way through the blinding rain. In the greyness two immense pillars, each with an enormous stone urn upon it, suddenly developed. Between them tall gates of rusty iron bars, with an upper line that dropped to a central device with a coronet in it, barred our way. They were chained and padlocked. From a low thatched cottage an old woman emerged and hailed us.

' Aren't ye frights altogether to be out a day the like o' this ! '

24

It was an assertion rather than an inquiry. We admitted our frightfulness and asked for the key of the gate.

' Sure it's not locked at all. Me son's below in the Park, striving to turn the horses this way for ye.'

We left the sheltering car and went forth into what felt like the end of the world that was being reduced to its primary element, when the earth was without form and void, and darkness was upon the face of the deep. We were in the ancient park of the Lords X——, three hundred acres or more in extent, with cloudy groups of splendid trees dimly visible. We slopped onwards over wastes of coarse grass that was apparently growing in water. Presently we were at the brink of a river. Had we pursued our way across it we could hardly have been wetter, but, as we considered it, out of the mist a group of about a couple of dozen of young horses came galloping towards us, led by a yellow mare, with her black tail in the air, flourishing sideways. They swung away from us, a collie dog yapping at their heels. Close behind came a young man, panting and red-faced.

' They'll go to the big gates——' he shouted. ' Let yees come on——'

We came on. The young man explained, breathlessly, that the one we were to see was the little chestnut that was next after the yalla mare, the Shan Bui, ' him with the white blaze. He's clean bred ! '

25

They were clustered by the gates when we got up to them, facing us, full of suspicion. The little chestnut's white blaze showed where he stood a little apart from the rest. My counsellor and I advanced cautiously, but a hasty glance was all that was permitted to us. The Shan Bui mare hoisted her black flag, and the party were off again, squealing and kicking.

But with that hasty glance my heart had gone out to the little chestnut. I said I would buy him.

My counsellor could hardly speak, such was the shock. He said how could I buy him? I hadn't as much as put a hand on him.

To 'put a hand', in this connexion, implies prolonged feeling of legs, of peering into eyes, of implanting chins or noses in or on withers—a ceremony lengthier, and as important as a marriage service.

But I was too wet to argue.

And so, two years later, the little chestnut and the black crossed the ocean together, and Love at First Sight had not been blind.

But I have never been allowed to forget that it is no way to go to buy a horse without as much as putting a hand on him.

IV

THE FIELD

I THINK it is undeniable that between the Officials of any Hunt and its Followers there is ever a secret, what may be called a subcutaneous hostility. Yet Hunt Establishments cannot, as a rule, exist without subscribers, and as these, naturally, form the foundation of the Field, this feeling seems impolitic, if not illogical.

But let me begin at the normal beginning of my typical day, which is the Meet, and at a Meet, given satisfactory weather, these crumples in rose-leaves are not apparent. The Master—who is more often than not also the Huntsman—exhibits successfully an early morning affability, and has, if astute, a special greeting for recent subscribers. The First Whip—who is, if less ostensibly, more often than not also the Huntsman, if not the Master—is accessible, friendly, and, also if astute, optimistic as to the Sport that may be expected. It is the moment to encourage, and, as one might say, 'jolly' the riders, who are still individuals, and

27

not as yet amalgamated into that sinister combination, the Field.

The five minutes of ' Law ' for late-comers has elapsed. The Master, with an eye, that is already baleful, on a few carefully unobtrusive motor-cars, moves off down the road towards the patch of woodland that is to be the first draw The Hounds, who have been seated by the roadside in bored resignation, wake to alert hopefulness ; the Whip utters a few encouraging chirps.   The curtain is up, the stage set.

At the Master's stirrup shuffles the Earth-stopper, like all his race, a master of imaginative fiction.   From his assurances it might seem a risk to take Hounds into the wood confided to his care, lest they should be outnumbered and devoured by the foxes.

' It wasn't but ere yesterday,' he says, ' I seen him and his four young ones on the rock behind my house, saluted against the sky.   It would have delighted ye ! '

The Master notes the useful simplification of the word silhouetted, while aloud, he says, sardonically, that he hopes they're not all stopped in, as they were the last time.

The protests of the wounded Earth-stopper are cut short by the Field Master, an elderly gentleman in a very old scarlet coat and a velvet cap, who, for this is Ireland, is almost certainly a Major or a Captain.   He has joined the Master for confidential instructions.   The following Field watch the conjunction with deep suspicion.   It is impossible to persuade them that they are not about to be penned in a position that will ensure their losing the Hunt.

The Master and Hounds jump a low wall and are lost to sight in the wood. The Whip gallops away into infinity. The Field is instructed to keep quiet, and stay where it is on the road. At least, they grumble to each other, they can see one side of the road. It might be worse.

They fall to gossip and, being an Irish Field, to politics. There are not more, perhaps, than fifteen to twenty, all told. Of these nearly half are ladies, and there are, almost inevitably, two or three doctors. It may be noted that in Ireland the Medical Profession seems to find that ever on hunting days there is a marked improvement in the condition of patients. There are, perhaps, four or five young men, three of them young soldiers on leave and hirelings, and a few farmers, mounted, most of them, on the excellent Old Irish-bred cart-mares, who do all and every sort of work, and as often as not add a likely foal to their yearly good deeds.

Among the farmers is the Veterinary Surgeon of the district, riding a green four-year-old. He is much courted by the farmers, and is addressed by them as Doctor. His lightest utterance is passed from mouth to mouth reverentially. Nothing but the heels of the four-year-old preserve him from being inextricably hemmed in by his admirers when the moment of release occurs.

To the waiting Field it seems that this is never coming.

Mutinous whispers are exchanged. It is said that He—He is the Master—will go away on the far side without letting us know, as he did before. A farmer says with finality :

'He's not in it.' (In this case He is the fox.)

Another replies tranquilly :

'And if he was itself, they'll not stir him.'

The Farmers are perfectly content, and ask no better than to sit and talk, discussing in minute detail the horses that surround them.

A rebel girl, remarking that she is bored stiff and won't stick it any longer, detaches herself from her fellows and goes up to the Field Master, and says with impudence thinly veiled in humility :

'Please, Captain, may I go home ?'

The Field Master, who is old and wise, and has known her from her first pony, when she was five years old, cocks an eye at her and replies :

'Certainly, my dear, but I'd advise that you wait awhile.'

The rebel—who, as a matter of fact, has no intention of going home till the Hounds do the same—retires, and says shamelessly to her fellows that the old pig won't let her go.

The day has clouded over, and a slight drizzle has begun, but sure that's no harm, say the farmers. The old Field Master turns up his collar. No one else notices it.

Presently, from the far end of the covert, a very faint shout is heard.

'That's like it!' says the Vet.

A tremor runs through the little waiting company like a wind through a wood. The Field Master holds up his hand. Then a scarlet coat appears at the end of the trees, and a cap is held up. It is responded to by the heart-shaking doubled notes of the horn.

'He's blowing them out!' pants the Field.

The next instant the Master is seen, going hard. That white smear, sweeping uphill across the plough at the end of the covert, is the Hounds. Their cry comes down the wind to the Field.

'Away with ye now!' says the Field Master, beginning to gallop.

The Vet.'s four-year-old goes straight into the air. Before he touches ground again the girls and the doctors are ahead of him, and the hirelings of the lads on leave are fleeing, as is appointed to hirelings, and are hardly stopped at the point where the Hounds crossed the road, to let the Master go on.

Away over the high pastures goes the Hunt, the cattle scattering before the Hounds. There is nothing to stop even the prudent farmers, who none the less diverge by deep-rooted instinct to the gaps in every fence.

'How would they drive in the cows without there'd be

gaps ? ' they say, eyeing philosophically the thrusters taking the tall grassy banks in the direct footsteps of the Master and the Hounds. The fox has turned, and is leaving the high country, taking a slanting course downwards over the grass towards a valley with a swift little river running through it. The Field is already widely distributed. Some follow the farmers, some the Vet. The Whip has a tail like a kite, composed of the meek in spirit, who have no false pride about taking a line for themselves, and mean to be in the hunt. In the valley the going is less agreeable. The Hounds skim over a tract of bog where horses cannot follow. A rash youth who attempts to do so gets into a soft place ; his friends callously leave him to be salvaged by country-men, who, as is usual, are developed out of space when an accident occurs. The Hunt splashes across a river, and is faced by a rough and steep hill. The pitiless Hounds sweep on, the horses toil after them, thinking, no doubt, what a fine thing it would be if, like the Hounds, they had only themselves to carry. There follows a long tract of heathery moorland country, with well-dispositioned walls, made of round stones, and not high enough to stop any one. The Field is thinned, but is still persevering.

' He's for Cooragannive,' says the Vet., pulling his now-chastened four-year-old on to his feet as he pecks on landing over a wall. ' We'll have time to draw our wind there——'

' I'd have no sort of objection to a check,' puffs a stout

'HE'S BLOWING THEM OUT!'

and perspiring Doctor. No more will his mare, who wishes she were in the shafts, jogging to the Dispensary.

The fox has run parallel with the river, and the Chase is now nearing the long wood of Cooragannive, that hangs from the crest of the high ground down to the water's edge. A mob of mountainy cattle are careering in front of the Hounds, who have begun to run slowly and with less conviction, and now, still at some distance from the wood, throw up their heads.

'He's in it to be sure,' says the Master, looking at his watch. 'Twenty-nine minutes—call it thirty. I'm two and a half couple short——'

He sends the Whip back for them, and surveys the wood dubiously. It is a formidable proposition.

What remains of the Field, still full of going, but thankful for the check, arrive. One girl's pony, quite undefeated, dashes at full gallop into the middle of the group.

'She's running away all the time!' wails the rider, as a couple of hounds narrowly escape destruction. The girl's hair has broken loose. She explains in strident tones that Nell was pulling so hard, and she couldn't see because her hair was in her eyes, and she knocked Kathleen into a ditch, and——

Here a roar from the Master commands silence.

'But I believe I've *killed* Kathleen!' screams the girl indignantly, 'I *must* say that!'

34

'Ah, nonsense,' says the Field Master. 'Look at her coming up now!'

The Master turns furiously on the rapidly advancing Kathleen.

'Keep back!' he shouts, not without some intensifying additions, 'keep back out o' that!'

'But I'm nowhere!' shrieks Kathleen in reply, 'I'm only arriving!'

The Field laughs unsympathetically, yet with comprehension.

The Master turns on the Field Master.

'For God's sake, Captain, take the damned Field out of this!' Then, with a yell to the Whip to put the Hounds on to him, he charges at the tall briary fence of the wood, and in a moment, such as have survived of the Field see all that at present makes life worth living, lost to them. The girls turn upon the old Field Master.

'Captain! Captain!' they cry, 'What shall we do now?'

The Captain is lighting a pipe He looks over the flaring match and says :

'Cooragannive will hold him a good half-hour. There's an old saying, "If ye can't be aisy, be as aisy as ye can!"' He winks at the stout Doctor. 'That's about it, Doctor, what?' he says cheerfully, and starts his pipe into action.

The Field is resentful. Two of the soldiers set forth

alone round the end of the wood to find out what is happening. They promise to bring tidings. The rest, with a various selection of adjectives with reference to the weather, which has now relapsed into steady rain, produce cigarettes. The girls agree about the weather and accept cigarettes. A certain calm is established. The hirelings eat grass voraciously. The riders find a solace in exchanging autobiographical details of the run up to date, with footnotes as to former exploits.

Half an hour elapses, and still there is no sign from the Wood of Cooragannive. Only the Hunt Terrier, who has been industriously hunting rabbits, appears on the top of the fence and is emulously given chocolate by the young ladies.

'Give him to me,' says the Captain. 'He's done enough and so have I. I'll take him home.' He takes off his old velvet cap. 'Good-bye to you all !' he says, riding away with the little dog in his arms.

The doctors decide to follow him. They say they've had a nice bit of a hunt, and isn't a good half-hour enough for any one ? And what's more, the rain's coming on heavy. Interchanging dark professional statistics as to the cases that await them, they depart.

The rest of the small party consult, and decide to proceed along the hill, above the wood.

'We might hear something or meet somebody,' they say hopefully

It is a long way, and involves a series of *détours* to avoid impossibilities of rock and bog. Nothing is to be seen. The country, through the grey veils of rain, looks as bereft of human life as it might have appeared shortly after the Creation, before the arrival of Adam and Eve. The Field find themselves on a narrow stony road, and straggle onwards in uncertainty. At last two red specks appear in the distance, and are greeted with excitement and relief.

'There they are!' 'But where are the Hounds?'

The red specks materialize into the two of their number who had set forth alone. Bitter disappointment.

'We could make out nothing,' they say drearily.

After a mile or two more of the stony road, the depressed and derelict Field encounter a man leading a donkey laden with panniers of turf.

Hope revives.

'Did you see the Hounds?' they shout at him in chorus.

After a few repetitions of the inquiry it penetrates the man's intelligence.

'I did not,' he says composedly.

'Think now, like a good man,' says somebody entreatingly. 'We know they were in the wood a while ago. Are you sure you didn't hear them?'

'I did not,' says the man, nodding his head. He gives the donkey a slight kick in the stomach, and says:

'G'wan!'

'I SEEN TWO JOCKS ABOVE ON THE HILL OVER

Then, as he is starting, he adds a postscript :
' But I seen two jocks above on the hill over.'
The Field thrills.
' That was them ! ' they shout, regardless of grammar.
' Splendid ! We'll meet them yet ! '
' Are ye sure the Hounds weren't with them ? ' says
another, cautiously.
' I am not,' says the man. ' It might be they were.'
' Ah, come on ! ' cries the Field in unison. ' Hurry !
We'll find them now ! That was them of course ! '
They snatch up their reins, the horses are conscious of a
stir, and brighten up.
One of the soldiers hesitates.
' Look here,' he says to the man, ' whereabouts exactly
were they when you saw them ? '
The man, with an awakening glimmer of intelligence,
looks at him.
' Why-then, I b'lieve one o' them was yoursel'. It was
a sheshnut horse he was on, with white legs——'
He has described with accuracy the inquirer's hireling.

The Field return home, in heavy rain, whither the
Master, the Whip, and the Hounds have preceded them by
nearly an hour.

V

THE KENNEL-TERRIER

IT is not too much to say that no one would be more shocked and surprised at being relegated to, as it were the Heel of the Hunt, than the person, or perhaps one might more properly say the Personage, to whom these later thoughts refer. It is indeed almost with awe that one reflects on the greatness of soul, the self-respect, the self-consciousness (a quality that is attributed—erroneously, as I believe—to man only) of a very small terrier.

Especially are these present in the terrier that is accredited to a pack of Foxhounds. When it is considered what it can accomplish with that tiny rough body, those indomitable little legs, that absurdly small head, packed with constructive intelligence yet with a brain-pan no bigger than an apple, it is impossible to deny that its high opinion of itself is justified.

There was once a little white rough dog who was—or thought he was—in charge of a small pack of Foxhounds in the South of Ireland. He was born of a noted strain of his sort, in very distinguished surroundings, no less than the Kildare Hunt Establishment, and perhaps it was as well that, like Joseph, he was sold into captivity when he was too young to realize how very far he had come down in the world, geographically and otherwise. But, like Joseph, he soon rose to eminence. He was little more than a year old

A PERSONAGE

when his career as a Hunt terrier began, and the way in which he recognized and adapted himself to the conditions of his job came little short of genius. He soon realized the need of conserving his strength, and submitted to being parted from the Pack and carried by any available means to the Meet. Once there, however, he would break from control and asserting himself as a foxhound among fox-hounds, would become merged with the Pack.

But he had a technique of his own. Realizing that to

41

struggle through the intricate jungles of those southern haunts of the Fox would exhaust him unduly before the more serious business began, he would, as soon as the Hounds were thrown into covert, post himself outside it on a convenient hillock, and there would sit, rigid, ears pricked, waiting for the first questioning note. When it came he

'ON A CONVENIENT HILLOCK'

would spring to attention. One could see that every fibre of his little body was hearkening for the next, and when certainty followed, Tatters—such was his unassuming name —like an arrow from the bow, would join his comrades, and in any interval of the melodious hound-music, his small shrieks would fill the silence.

In the wild country which had become his, there are

seldom runs that do not find their earthly close in a drain or gully, or similar place of refuge. Many were the occasions when the Hounds, having Marked to Ground, would be found vainly endeavouring to thrust the greater, themselves, into that which could only contain the less, the Fox. The Huntsman, dragging by the stern a futile enthusiast out of the mouth of the hole, might then be seen looking over his shoulder, and asking, with pardonable violence, where that tarrier had got to. 'And then,' as Lord Macaulay has said—certain quotations are so applicable that they must be corrupted to my purpose—'Then,' I repeat, 'the cry is "Tatters !" and lo, the ranks divide, and——' but the quotation ceases to apply, for it is less like the stately stride of the Great Lord of Luna than a bullet leaving a gun, that Tatters comes through the Field. He bores his way like an eel or an augur into the clamouring Pack, and if there is—as there generally is—a back-door to the drain, it is seldom long before the Fox has decided to leave by it, and, since the Hounds have been removed to a reasonable distance, the waiting and watching Field can view his retreat, relentlessly pursued by a little creature that is now dark brown and half its normal size, because drains are usually wet and muddy.

The Fox melts away—impossible to express the imperceptible way in which a fox can disappear. Even though he is—as an excited follower avers—the size of a chestnut horse, he is in a single instant incredibly lost to sight. The Hounds are laid on. Tatters is overtaken. Not so the Fox. In that hilly country of rocks and gullies and of what, locally, are spoken of as 'His Dungeons', he, having been given his chance, far more often than not, takes it.

Little Tatters soon became the idol of the Huntsman's heart. Every indulgence was his. Rats, served up in a lordly trap, to gratify his zest for blood. The choicest

'TATTERS WAS A HAPPY LITTLE DOG'

morsels from the Hounds' kitchen. A barrel packed with straw and placed, in winter, as near the boiler-stove as possible. Even though those Kennels were not those of the Killing Kildares, Tatters was a happy little dog. A bride was found for him, white, like himself, with fascinating fair hair (her ears only, and one spot on her back) and with the similar tastes, for rats and petty robbery, that are so all-important in ensuring a happy married life. The little couple were established at the Huntsman's cottage, in due season a daughter blessed their union, and, for a time, all went well.

Unfortunately, however, Tatters began after a time to regard the comfortable cottage kitchen as his Capua, and craved for the original and sterner barrel at the Kennels. He had early developed a passion for the Dog-Hounds. He preferred their society even to that of his wife and daughter, and he lost no opportunity of slipping into their kennel and spending his days among them.

One morning, early in Tatters' third season, the Huntsman, with the Hounds, met the Master at the Kennel-gates as usual. They were going hunting. The Huntsman, a North-country little man, who had come from the Bramham Moor Hounds, saluted the Master, lifting his cap with solemnity, but said no word of greeting. Something was wrong. The Master said, not without anxiety :

' Hounds all right ? '

' I can't 'ardly bear to look at 'em ! ' was the remarkable response.

' Good heavens ! What's wrong ? '

' They've killed little Tattoo ! '

This was Tatters' pet name. Tears ran down the little Huntsman's red face.

' 'E got in among 'em last night, through the bars some way ; I suppose they was startled like and didn't know it was 'im——'

That was a sad day's hunting. And as if to emphasize the fact of the recent tragedy, the only fox, found after a long day of trailing over the hills, got to ground immediately, and there was no little Tatters to fetch him out.

The widowed Mrs. Tatters had never showed any fancy for the Chase. Her only game was rats, and even these without the late Tatters to back her up at critical moments, soon ceased to interest her. She developed *embonpoint* and kept the house.

Fortunately, however, their daughter, Scraps, had inherited her father's sporting tastes. At the time of his death she had just arrived at maturity. She had indeed already been occasionally taken out hunting with him, and the picture of the two little white things speeding after the pack, looking like demented grains of rice, is with me still. At the beginning of Scraps' career, before she had been established as official kennel-terrier, it was the Master's practice to take her, in company with an elderly Labrador, to a large walled-in place of seclusion, once an orchard, now given over to briars and bracken, and (which is more important) rabbits. There had Scraps been entered to her profession, and even though she knew that in the Season proper a nobler game was to be hers, yet she would collaborate with the Labrador with a very pretty enthusiasm, and on a system based on that of her father's in the field.

Regarding her comrade in the light of a tufter, she was

46

accustomed to send him into the briars to draw for the game, while she, on the central orchard path, struck appropriate attitudes.   Her height was but little more than eight inches—or it may be more respectful to say two hands—at the withers, yet her mien at such moments had the

THE STAND OF A BARB STALLION

arrogance and the splendour of the stand of a Barb stallion. Thus, tense and motionless, she would remain, her head held very high on a nobly arched neck ; her ears fiercely pricked, her tail at half-cock, her attention dramatically concentrated on the Tufter's probable position in covert.

The rabbit breaks.   The Labrador bursts into view in lumbering pursuit.   Scraps flings herself into action.   The

47

coarse grass and bracken are so high that it is possible to track her course only by a trail of squeaks, and by occasional glimpses of what looks like a hairy lawn-tennis ball, as she bucks through the long grass, running for blood. (It is, of course, well known that, in hunting through long grass, the Best Dogs, or at least, the Best Little Dogs, proceed in bucks, without reference to their noses, like kangaroos.) In these Orchard Hunts, the rabbit has never been known to fail to achieve safety considerably in advance of his pursuers ; a disappointment to which, however, invariable experience had inured them.

Agreeable to both Scraps and her owner as were these unofficial hunts, it must be confessed that it was to the taste they had encouraged that the owner owed a time of prolonged and acute anxiety. Within a few hundred yards of the Kennels were great cliffs that held the Atlantic at bay. They held also, unfortunately, what the Huntsman called ' a dose of rabbits '. To these cliffs, Scraps, slipping across the fields high above them, where sheep nibbled the salty grass, and rabbits disported themselves, would repair whenever she could elude supervision, and there, along the face of the cliffs, invisible among bushes and rocks, she would hunt, deaf to calls and whistles, only returning at her own pleasure.

And at last there came a night when she did not return. At day-break the search for her began, and so continued,

48

in despairing depression, for a long three days. Conviction was forced upon the searchers that she had either fallen from a cliff and been drowned, or had got wedged in a rabbit-hole and there had died. Search was abandoned.

It was a full four days later when

Late, late, in a gloaming, Kilmeny cam' hame.

A small, almost spectral form came creeping across the sheep-fields, and lay down, exhausted, unable to drag itself another inch, at the Kennel-door. Little Scraps had been starved free. Once before the same thing had happened to one of the Kennel-terriers, but in that unhappy case the cliffs had held their prey. Scraps' coat showed how tightly she had been jammed in the burrow. Her little body had wasted so thin that, like the dog in the fairy-tale, she might have been run through a wedding-ring. But starvation had saved her. She survived, and lived to end her days as pet and pampered Head-dog in the Master's home. There, despotically, she ruled the lesser dogs, and though the smallest of them all, her authority was unquestioned.

Even after her death in the fullness of time, she still kept her underlings in order. In life she had been accustomed when the mood took her, to leave her own comfortable basket and usurp that of a junior, a cushioned snail-shell, much coveted, though in no way superior to her own. It was not until after her death that the junior, whose name was Sheila, established undisputed possession of the desired basket. Yet, on a certain night, it was given to their owner to see Sheila's little snub nose poked out of the snail-shell, her eyes fixed very low down on the door. Something had come in. Sheila's little head followed the invisible visitor—

SOMETHING HAD COME IN

invisible to the grosser human being, though not to Sheila— round the room. Her rough little head was twisted round the side of the snail-shell, always at the same low level. Then, gingerly, she slid out of the basket. Glancing over her shoulder as she went, she stole across the room and went to ground under the sofa. Scraps, the Head-dog, had reasserted herself.

VI

DAN RUSSEL THE FOX

'DAN RUSSEL THE FOX', Chaucer calls him; 'Charles James', or, more affectionately, 'Charlie', English hunting-men will still speak of him. The ancient jest survives, dating from the time when Charles James Fox was only second to Reynard himself in public importance. It is possible that there may exist a few sportsmen as unaware as I, till recently, have been, of the origin of that still more ancient pet name, Reynard. But I say boldly that I doubt if many foxhunters could explain the title '*Goupil*' as relating to our old friend Br'er Fox.

It has happened that a hunting story, entitled 'The Pug-nosed Fox' (for which a certain Irish R.M. is responsible), has been translated into French, and '*Goupil le Camard*' has been the title chosen for it. Messrs. Bellows' French Dictionary, when appealed to, stated that '*camard*' meant 'blunt-nosed', but it coldly ignored the existence of such a noun as a ' *goupil* ', while it admitted the words ' *Goupille*, a pin ', and ' *Goupillon*, a Holy water sprinkler ', neither article suggestive of any possible connexion with a pug-nosed fox. So the translator was invoked, and he, a

OUR OLD FRIEND, BR'ER FOX

French cavalry officer, well versed in the two languages involved, gave the following explanation.

If one looks in a French Dictionary one finds ' *GOUPIL : vieux mot pour renard* '. Here is the story. Between 1400 and 1500 a *suite* of twenty-six poems has been written in France, and was called *Le Roman de Renart*. In these, animals were the heroes, and among them the most prominent were the Wolf and the Fox.

The writer goes on to say that in these stories the wolf received the proper name of Isengrin, and the fox, who was then known as the *goupil* (a name derived from the Latin *vulpes*), was given the proper name of Renart.

This name [says my authority] remains in the French language ever since to name a fox, although it was, when given to the *goupil*, only a special name. Nowadays, sometimes, when people talk about a fox they will name him *Goupil*. A few years ago a very good book has been published with the title *De Goupil à Margot*. That book dealt with stories about animals, from the Fox, *Goupil*, to the Magpie, *Margot*, and every one here will understand that *Goupil le Camard* means the Pug-nosed Fox.

The explanation was all that could be desired as far as it went, but the Holy Water Sprinkler had yet to be explained.

My authority did not fail me. He wrote :

Something else about *Goupil*. You mention having found the name *Goupillon* with which a priest throws Holy water, and I found that it was originally made with the tail of a fox !

A solution that defied conjecture and was too improbable not to be authentic.

The Foxhunter of sensibility is presented with difficulties more disturbing than these. Possibly sensibility is a quality to which Foxhunters are not entitled to claim, yet many Foxhunters, possibly, even, some Masters of Hounds, have known what it is to have torn sympathies as between a sinking fox and hard-working, disappointed hounds. For many it was one of the charms of that Southern Irish pack which has inspired most of these thoughts, that with Hounds as eager and thrusting as any Huntsman could desire, the ' blood ', which the Authorities declare to be indispensable as stimulant and incentive, was but seldom their portion. (And is it irrelevant to inquire if Fox-terriers eat rats?)

In the south-west of Ireland Dan Russel has unfailing allies in the rocks of his native hills, fortresses that but seldom fail him of an impregnable refuge, but I can remember at least one occasion when a very different sanctuary stood to him in the hour of need.

There came a day when a hill fox had incautiously gone hunting by daylight in comparatively open country and at some distance from his own domain. He had secured that which he required. The affair had gone pleasantly, and he was leaving for home with the fruit of his labours when the protests of the victim summoned her owner from her cottage. She, foaming maledictions, pursued Dan Russel, accompanied by an entirely inadequate cur-dog.

'An' little he regarded me, nor the poor thrash of a dog I has neether!' the owner, one Mrs. Cahalane, narrated later. 'Don't the people say always if ye'll call to a fox in Irish he'll let go what he has? But sure, this lad, Irish or English was the same to him, throttin' away for himself, cool an' aisy, and the best little hin I has hangin' out o' his mouth, screeching!'

Mrs. Cahalane paused to permit the fullness of her wrongs to sink in.

'But,' she resumed, 'wasn't it the Mercy o' God that the Hounds were in it the same day! I seen the Whip-man, from me, on the hill above me little house, an' I took the old shawl I has on me and I wove it to him ! " Look, Sir," says I, " it was that way he went ! " Well, if it was the Divil and all his Companions was in it, there wouldn't be more roaring out o' them than what them dogs had ! And, thanks be to the most divine God, me bold fox heard them and he a good mile away, an' he relaced me little hin ! I follied the thrack o' the feathers then till I got her, an' she half-dead, goin' screelum-scrawlum the two sides o' the field ! '

Thus the indignant Mrs. Cahalane, and thanks to her instructions to the Hunt, Dan Russel was hard put to it to save his life. They ran him on a burning scent over some three miles of the best bit of their country ; fair-sized pasture fields, for the most part, with room to gallop, and good honest jumps, not to mention a useful share of handy cattle-gaps. The fox was hardly five minutes ahead, the scent was like a path before the Hounds. They drove along it, rejoicing. Their cry was like the joy-bells at a Royal Wedding.

Dan Russel, making for his hill, heard them, and wondered if he could make it. Home and safety were still a good mile away, and he had had a poor start. A stream, born in the distant hill, fast-flowing and brown, cuts that part of that country in two. It also, as streams will, divided the riders into those who will and who won't jump water.

5

And, as it happened, the undecided were given time to consider the question. The Hounds knew no divided counsels. They cried their fox to the stream's edge, and then, leaping its dark flow from reedy bank to bank, they continued to chant what was to be the fox's funeral song. But they chanted it for no more than three lengths of a horse, and after a moment of uncertainty, flung themselves right and left, searching, silent now, and puzzled.

'Put 'em back!' shouts the Huntsman.

The baffled Hounds, glad of direction, hopeful of help, leaped back. Up and down along the margin of the stream they tried, and back across it again, but in vain. Lower down, the stream becomes wider and more shallow, the water coming dancing over gravel and stones, clear and golden as pale sherry. And just there it was that Bond-maid believed she had it. She put down her head and wet her muzzle, and with that, uttered a contralto note of conviction.

'Hark to Bondmaid! Bondmaid has it!'

Her comrades came hurrying to her, splashing through the racing water. Down the stream for some fifty yards went the old bitch, boasting her triumph, proud and confident. And all her fellows splashed after her. But the triumph was short-lived, and again the scent failed them. They were cast this side and that, among the rocks and furze-bushes on the farther side of the stream, and away over the boggy meadows that border it on the other, their many drains clouding its clearness. Not Bondmaid, nor Tarquin nor Tuneable could find a word to say, and when they fail there is no more to be said.

So the horn was touched, and the Hunt moved off, and no one had noticed a little black spot that had, a little way back, and at brief intervals, broken the surface of the smooth stream, just below the spot where the Hounds had first leapt across it. But a country boy, red-faced and panting, who had run after the Hunt for three long miles, reached the stream in time to see Dan Russel's nose emerge, followed by the rest of him. He climbed out and shook himself. His brush asserted itself authoritatively as a ' *Goupillon* '. Who shall say that the water that saved his life was not Holy Water ?

The eighteenth-century writers, and especially its poets, took a strong line, and calmed such sensibilities as they may have possessed by blackening the character of poor Reynard. ' Unruly Reynard ' he has been called by an old County Cork countrywoman whom he had despoiled.

' Unruly Reynard has me beggared ! ' she wrote.

The early poets dealt more faithfully with the enemy, acting on the sound principle that one should give a dog a bad name before hanging him. Certainly bad names were not spared. ' Traitor ', ' Villain ', ' Murderer '. A couple of centuries ago all the poets were loud in virtuous reprobation of Dan Russel.

> *The Fox who, all night, amidst darkness profound,*
> *On the sacred retirements of Innocence stole ;*
> *Now dreads retribution in ev'ry sound,*
> *And shrinks to the innermost depths of his hole.*
>
> *Let us, with calm bosoms, unconscious of wrong,*
> *All vile miscreants hunt down who on Innocence prey ;*
> *Nor lose sight of Virtue, in sports or in song,*
> *That our hearts may rejoice at the close of the day.*

When, as another poet, with a rather indifferent sense of rhythm, sings :

> *The savoury Surloin grateful smokes on the board*

and the turkey, that the vile miscreant failed to secure, is devoured by the virtuous sportsmen.

In these later times there is a more frank acceptance of the position. No such effort at justification is attempted, and the aphorism that ' nothing in his life became him like the leaving it ' sums up the situation. After all, the alternative for Unruly Reynard is traps, and poison, and extinction ; Horse and Hound and Horn give him at least a sporting chance for life, and the Hunt Fowl-Fund pays his butcher's bill.

It was once, long ago, my good fortune to have some hunting with the cream of England's classic packs of Foxhounds, an experience strangely remote from those bestowed by the hunts that have, for the most part, inspired these thoughts. There came a day when I had the luck of a great run with one of the most distinguished of the packs of the 'Shires', over a wonderful smooth galloping country of broad meadows, all provided with gates that actually opened and closed as required, with not so much as one 'single-stone-gap' among them, and with such incredibly beautiful, trim, and solid hedges that an Irish mare thought to change feet on the first she had to cross, and only saved herself by virtue of possessing, like most Irish hunters, a fifth leg that she held in reserve for emergencies.

Evening had come before the long hunt ended, and the 'Sporting Chance', that had served Dan Russel many times, had failed him at last. There had followed a cere-mony which, to one onlooker, seemed such a strange and archaic rite as might have been instituted by 'Bahram that Great Hunter', what time he kept hounds in Nineveh.

The black-whiskered Huntsman—an elderly formalist, who, faithful to tradition, still wore, close-clipped, these trade marks—was standing on the slope of a grassy hill, high against the sky, holding the stiffened body of the fox in both hands above his head. Already the *rigor mortis* had made it its own. Those of the Field that had survived the long hunt were grouped a little below. The Whippers-in had ranged the pack in a half-circle facing their Huntsman ;

their horses stood patiently in the background, glad enough, I dare say, of a pause in the day's long work. The Hounds waited, submissive, in the place appointed to them, their beautiful faces set on the Huntsman; the yellow evening light gilded them, and lit the scarlet coats of the men. Then the Huntsman stooped and propped the fox's body,

'A STOUT HILL-FOX'

standing on its four legs, in the middle of the circle of the Hounds, that were waiting, tense, expectant. It stood there rigid. The Huntsman waited an instant before he uttered the Who-Whoop that tells the end has come. The Whippers-in loosed the wild screams that seem to have in them the barbaric ecstasy of primitive hunters.

'Twas a stout hill-fox when they found him,
Now 'tis a hundred tatters of brown!

60

VII

LITTLE RED RIDING-HOOD IN KERRY

MOIRA CLOCA-DEARG—(and that means, in Irish, Mary of the Red Cloak, and the way you'd say it in English is ' Cloaka-dharrig ')—was a nice young girl of about seventeen years. She lived with her mother, a decent widow-woman by the name of Margaret Sheehan, who had a small handy little farm that wasn't maybe more than a couple o' miles out from the town of Caherciveen in the County Kerry.

The neighbours put the name of Cloca-dearg on Moira, for she having a tasty red coat, and a hood on it, that the Mother made for her to wear when she'd be riding after the hounds.

It might be thought a strange thing and against nature that a small farmer's daughter would have the way and the fancy to follow hounds. But sure these weren't grand

English quality hounds at all. They were no more than only them big black dogs, Kerry Baygles they calls them, that the farmers' sons keeps to be hunting the foxes, that wouldn't leave a hen nor a goose in the country if they'd be let alone. And it was the way Moira seen pictures in the town of hunters in red coats, and after she getting the pony, the world wouldn't content her without she'd get a red coat the same as she seen in the pictures.

But wait till I tell you how she got the pony that was as near and dear to her as the blood of her arm.

She had the fancy always to be going away by herself in lonely places. She would be by the way of going to school —that was a good two miles back in the town—and the Mother would give her a bit of soda-bread and one o' them hot-bottles with milk, for her lunch. But maybe in place of going to school at all, she would stray away in the hills, and queer stories she would bring back with her to the Mother.

One day it was a little old manneen that was no higher than her knee that met her, and requested her in Irish would she come with him to the Fort above on Slieve Liath, and see the neat pair of shoes he was making for one of the High Quality there, and he said he might make as good a pair for herself, once he had the length of her foot. She hadn't but ten years then, but as young as she was, she had sense. She thanked him kindly, but she told him she

'OH, MY DARLING LITTLE PONY-EEN!' SAYS SHE

had all the shoes she wanted. Sure she knew well enough
it was a Cluricaune he was, and if she put a foot into a
shoe he made, if it was into the lake he went itself, she
should follow him. She told the Mother how she had met
the Cluricaune, and that he had a neat red cap on him,
and a deeshy-daushy little leather apron, and a nice civil
little old lad he was too, and good company. The Mother
cautioned her she had no business keeping such company.
But sure the world wouldn't stop her roaming that way.
Every once in a while she'd come home and say to the
Mother she seen this and that—a child, maybe, that she'd
think was going astray, and she'd hear it crying, and
would run after it different ways, and when it had her tired
out, it'd soak away into the hill from her. Or she'd hear
like laughing in the air, or horns blowing. There are plenty
would friken at the like o' that, but sure that was all like
nothing to Moira Cloca-dearg, for her being so used to it.
And another day it might be the little manneen that she
might see, from her, like, and he'd be gone again in the
minute, but he might wave the red cap to her, like he was
friendly to her.

There was a day when the Widow Sheehan had a couple
o' hundred cabbage-plants to set for her cows, and says she
to Moira :

'Ye're so great with the fairies, it's a pity ye wouldn't
ask them would they give me a hand to set the cabbages.'

Well, that I may never sin, if the next morning she didn't find the cabbage plants all set, but where were they growing only in the path down from the hill to the cottage ! The poor woman had to give the day digging them out, and setting them where they should be in the potato-garden. And wasn't that like a lesson to Moira she should keep out from the like o' them ? But divil a hair did she care.

Moira was about thirteen years when her Mother sent her to go back in the hills to look for a milking-goat that had gone astray on her. The little girl was searching the hill, hither and over, till she was beat out entirely, and in the finish, when she could get no trace of the goat at all, she sat down to rest herself by one of them old forts that was back on the hill, Dun-na-shee it was called for being a place that the old people said was greatly resorted to by the fairies. Moira sat down on a big stone that was beside the ope in the wall of the fort. It was very early of a summer morning and the grass was grey with the dew. She heard a sound of music inside in the fort. Very light and sweet it was, and it came out to her through the ope in the wall. It went past her then where she was sitting. As the music went past her she saw the dew brushing away off the grass, like that people were passing, but not a sign of e'er a one could the little girl see.

Well, as tired as she was, she rose up and she followed the music. She told the Mother, after, she'd nearly have

64

to dance it was that jolly. She hadn't gone above twenty perches when she came to a level place, with good grass and ferns, and a stream running through it, and a great growth of fox-gloves, that the people say is a great fairy plant—'Fairy Fingers' they calls it, but Lusmore is the name in Irish for it—growing thick by the stream, as gay as a garden. The stream was running out from under a big rock the size of a house, and beyond the stream, lying down under the rock in the grass, so cosy, what was there but me goat ! And standing beside her, taking a sup of water for itself, there was a pure white yearling pony ! As white as the drivelling snow it was. You'd hardly see the like in a circus.

The music went winding on always. Round the far end of the big rock it went, but sure Moira Cloca-dearg forgot it entirely when she seen the pony.

' O my darling little pony-een !' says she, and she crossed the stream to the pony, and the creature stood, like as if it knew her, and looked at her as wise as a man. It was about the size of a good ass.

' O if I could carry you home with me !' says Moira, petting it.

' Ho, Ho, Ho !' says it, like it was agreeable to go with her.

She turned about then and roused up the old goat, and she said good-bye like to the pony—for how could she drive the two of them ?—and she started to drive the goat down the hill. She was hardly past the level ground and going on down the glen, when she heard a sound behind her, and what was it but the white pony following after her !

When Moira saw the pony coming on this way, she was greatly delighted.

' Come along, my little jewel,' she says ; ' we'll live and die together ! '

In the minute she heard a screech of laughter from back up the hill, and a horn blew a salute, like what a huntsman would blow when he seen the fox starting to run away. But Moira didn't mind at all.

' Blow away ! ' says she, ' I have her now and I'll keep her ! ' says she, ' and Lusmore is the name I'll put on her, for finding her where she was, with the Fairy Fingers around her ! '

But look, from that day out the fairies had a spite agin her.

That now was how she got the pony. Every step of the way home it followed her, and when the Mother seen it she was delighted altogether. ' For,' says she, ' in two years' time it'll be grown, and many a good basket o' turf it'll carry for us ! '

Moira made her no answer, but says she to herself, ' It's me it'll be carrying, and not turf at all ! '

The Widow Sheehan had a near neighbour by the name

of John Wolfe. His farm was next to hers, and the name of it was Caherbrech, which means the Fort of the Wolves, and long ago they say there was wolves there in plenty. I believe there was one of them patriots one time by the name of Wolfe Tone, but John Wolfe had no call or claim to him ; he was no patriot at all, but a quiet, respectable man, with no wish for fighting, and having a nice stall of cows, and a good share of money put away in the bank.

But the son he had was a wild lad. Cornelius was his name, and Curley Brech was the name the people had for him, and there was no mischief and tricks done in the country but what he was at the back of them. His near way to school was through the Widow Sheehan's ground, and it was hardly he'd pass her house without he'd do some mischeevious thing to her property or herself. He was older than Moira by three years, and he was the divil's own play-boy, and never tired with tormenting her and her Mother.

And as he got older it was only worse and more torment-ing he grew. He was for ever running after Moira, and bringing by the way of presents for her Mother, pounds of butter, or a leg of pork when his father'd have a pig killed ; but if he did, he'd hide them in some wrong place, like one time when he had a comb of honey for her, and where did he leave it only in her bed, and didn't the poor woman throw herself down on it, and the curses she put out of her'd fill a house, and her own child only to laugh at her ! And there wouldn't be a day hardly that he'd not be teasing Moira. He was a great play-actor, and as full of tricks as a fairy. He'd be waiting in an amberbush, maybe, to lep out at her, with an old hat on him, the way he'd be a tramp, and then letting on to console her, and trying to kiss her when she'd be crying with the fright—the raging scamp ! And another day he might steal his Mother's old clothes and dress himself like an old woman, and come begging to the Widow for a sup o' tay for God's sake. And when the creature'd have it made—for mind ye she was charitable that way—nothing would content the old *calliach* that he let on to be. It'd be too wake, or too strong, or he didn't want but the colour of milk and she had it drowned with cream, or it was rotten with sugar, and the like o' that. The Widow would get mad entirely, and would bid him walk out of her house, and then the lad would begin to strip the old clothes off of him and throw them on the floor, and herself'd think it was a madwoman he was, and would roar for the Polis, God help her, with the Barracks two miles away !

Didn't he go one winter night with a pot of that red raddle that they mixes in whitewash, and he painted Lusmore, the white pony, with big patches of red, the same as a cow. When Moira went in the dark morning to feed her she thought it was a cow was in it.

' O Mother, Mother ! ' says she, giving the big mouth, ' the Fairies have me pony stole away, and a little rackling of a heifer left in place of her ! '

It wasn't till the pony roared to her for her feed that she knew her. The Mother and Moira gave the day washing her, and in spite of them she was as red as a new-born child for a week after.

The pony was up to three years when Curley Brech done this to her, and a fine stout puck of a pony she was too. Moira would ride her far and near in a grand saddle that had two crooked horns on it, the same as a Kerry cow. The Mother got it one time at an Oxtion.

' Here ! ' says the Oxtioneer, ' the man that brings this home'll get a kiss that'd wather a horse ! '

' I want no kisses,' says the Widow Sheehan. ' I'll bid ye two pound for the saddle, and divil blow the ha'penny more I'll give ! ' And faith, she got it.

It was then Moira started to follow the Hounds, and the Mother made her the tasty red riding-coat, and she put a hood on it, the way the girl'd cover her head if the weather'd be bad, and it was then the people put the name of Clocadearg on her.

Every Sunday and every Holy-day the boys would be out with the hounds. Eighteen dogs o' them there were of the black Baygles, and they'd mostly have a couple of bracket hounds—that's the way you'd say ' spotted ' in English—

white they'd be and black and brown spots on them, like them English hounds. They has the like o' them the way you'd see them away from you when the black dogs would hardly be seen at all, for the hills being so dark like. They were strewed out through the country. One lad'd have two, and maybe another three, and another might have but the one. Each hound would follow his own till they'd all be met together, and then they should be answerable to the horn. And who was the lad that had the horn only me bold Curley Brech! He was the leader for them, and an arch boy he was, that could run like a hound himself, and was as cute as a pet fox, let alone a mountainy one! All the lads followed after the dogs on their own legs, but if Moira got the chance when the Mother wouldn't know, she'd pounce up on the pony, and away with her after the hunt!

The way the huntsmen had, they'd drive the dogs before them till they'd find a fox, or maybe start a hare, and if it was a hare, that'd run back and forth round a valley, the boys would wait on a hill above and see the hunt, and run down and take the hare from the hounds if they cot her. But if it was a fox they had, it might be dark night before the lads'd see them again, and it'd be no better for Moira, and she on a mountainy pony that could run on the rocks like a bird. But sure the fox'd take the hounds away entirely, where horse nor man couldn't follow them.

As sure as Moira would be in the hunt it'd always be a fox they'd find, and back in the mountains he'd carry the dogs, and as sure as there's a harp on a ha'penny that'd be the fox they'd never ketch !

'And why not ? ' says you.

Because it'd be a fairy fox sure ! It was the spite the fairies had agin Moira, for carrying away the white pony, that they'd keep a fox handy, and the dogs never be let ketch him, and them and Moira'd be put astray, and it might be dark night before she'd get home or the dogs either. Half-dead they'd all be, and the pony the worst of all.

Well, there was a fine day came in Febbiverry, it was Valentine's Day—(and by the same token, that year it was the last day of Shraft)—and Moira was eighteen years the same day. Her Mother says to her :

' Ketch the pony,' says she, ' and throw the saddle on her, and you'll go see your Grannema, and bring her the nice present that I have for her, and maybe yourself'd get a present from her, for this being your birthday. And,' says the Mother, says she, looking at Moira very sevare, ' Let you go straight there, and no idling and gosthering with any that'd be in your road, and if you meet that limb o' the divil, Curley Brech, mootching and purshawling,' says she, ' give him the go-by, cool and nice,' says she. ' Leave him go his way and you go yours.'

'Faith and I will too!' says Moira, '*I've* no wish for him, or the likes of him!' says she, as proud as the Queen of Spain.

The Mother then puts a nice pat o' fresh butter, and a nice comb o' honey, and a lovely soda loaf, and a dozen fresh eggs in a basket, and Moira puts on her new red riding-coat, and away with her to ride across the hill to the Grandmother. (The grandmother was old Mrs. Dan Sheehan, that was Moira's grandmother by the father. She had a power o' money, and the Widow Sheehan, that was her daughter-in-law, was for ever sending Moira to see her, and paying her little compliments of eggs and butter, and the like o' that.)

Moira wasn't gone farther than John Wolfe's farm when who would she see before her only Curley Brech, and two hounds with him, and one of them was a big black baygle, by the name of Bugler, and the other was a little young bracket bitch, whose name was Comfort; and them was the two best hounds in the country.

Curley Brech ketches the pony by the head, and puts his arm over her neck. The pony wasn't but fourteen hands, and Curley was a tall straight boy.

'Where are ye goin'?' says he to Moira, grinning at her, and shaking her by the hand, and not letting it go. 'So smart ye look in your red ridin'-coat, darlin'!' says he.

'*I'm* not your darlin'!' says Moira, pulling the hand

from him (but sure she couldn't keep from laughing at the impidence he had). ' For two pins I'd give ye a good box on the ear ! ' says she.

' Ah, ye would not ! ' says Curley Brech, coaxing her, and looking at her the way you'd say he'd like to eat her. ' And listen,' says he, ' I'm waiting now for the hounds, and let you wait too and have a hunt.'

' And what'll I do with me present for Grannema ? ' says Moira.

' I'll run back with it to me Mother,' says Curley, ' and can't ye get it from her when the hunt's over——'

Well now, that was where the mistake was for Moira. But to think of the hunt enticed her, and she was said by Curley Brech.

It was shortly then all the lads come along with the hounds, and me bold Curley outs with the horn, and off with them all up into the hill of Slieve Liath—that means the Grey Hill, but green and sunny it was that fine Valentine's Day, and sure a person's heart'd rise on a day like it, and the hounds playing around, and hunting through the rocks, and putting yowls out o' themselves if they seen as much as a rabbit or a weasel in the heather before them.

Curley Brech, with the horn, went on before the other lads, giving a shout now and again to hearten the hounds, and walking beside the pony, and looking at Moira, and saying to her to tell him when she seen a fox, ' for none of

us,' says he, looking up at her so tender, ' has the sight to
see a fox the way your blue eyes can ! '

Moira wouldn't let on she heard him, but Curley seen
the blush on her cheek, and he knew by her she was pleased.

They weren't gone deep into the hill at all when what'd
Moira see close beside them, only the little Cluricaune, and
he sitting on a flat rock and the tools of his trade beside
him. He took the red cap off of his head and he wove it
to her. Moira returned him a salute.

' Who are ye saluting at all ? ' says Curley, looking
around, but sure he hadn't *the Sighth*, the way Moira had.
But old Bugler, that was the oldest of the hounds, saw the
manneen, and the hair stood up on the poor dog's back,
and he growled furious ; and Comfort, the little bracket
bitch, seen the manneen too, and she made a drive at him
to bite him, but in the minute he was gone, and no trace
of him on the rock !

' Ax no questions,' says Moira to Curley, teasing him,
' and ye'll be told no lies ! ' but she had it hardly said when
she seen the manneen again, standing up on the rock, and
waving his red cap up to the hill, saying ' Tally-Ho ! ' and
giving little small screeches, that not a one heard only
Moira, and old Bugler, and Comfort, the little bracket
bitch. Moira looks up at the hill, and what was there but
a big grey fox on a stretch of rock and he looking down at
them as cool as a Christian !

'Look at him above ! Look at him ! Look at him !' screeches Moira. 'Tally Ho forrad !' says she, and she comminces to gallop at the hill, with Lusmore, the white pony, pulling mad, and old Bugler and Comfort out ahead of her !

Well, then was the ecstasies ! Curley, and all the crowd of lads, shouting and legging it up the hill after Moira, and the hounds coming from all parts and sweeping through the crowd ! Believe me, the fox didn't wait long ! What a fool he'd be, with them black Baygles, like Black Death itself, yowling after him ! They gethered like bees on the rock he was on, and then old Bugler threw up his head, and 'Yow ! Yow ! Yow !' says he. 'Here's the way he went !' says he. And Comfort, the little bracket bitch, give a squeal like ye'd say it was a pig and it having the throat cut, and away on the line goes the two o' them, and all the rest o' the dogs roaring after them !

By the mercy o' God there was a good cattle-track going up the glen. Up it goes Moira, with the pony pulling like she wanted to ketch the fox herself, and all the lads coming on after her, and Curley Brech blowing his horn for fear would any hounds be behind them (but faith, it wasn't long before the breath failed him !). When they got to the top of the glen, there was a level place that wasn't level entirely, for it slanted up to another rise of hill. The hounds had it nearly crossed when Moira got up to it. Boggy it was, but

75

not too deep ; she faced the pony at it, and sure the pony went away over it as easy and independent as a snipe, and Curley and the boys following on always.

On the hill beyond the bog they could see the hounds, but hardly. Them black hounds when they gets away in the heather, melts like into it. You'd nearly say it was a shadow only you saw, if it wasn't for Comfort, the bracket bitch, that showed where they were. White she was, and spotted, and a yellow head on her, like her dam, that was an English hound John Wolfe had one time. Great hounds to hunt they are, and the cry they had was like a band o' music, and the sound went beating from one hill to another, most lovely.

As tired as the boys were, they couldn't stop running with that in their ears, and with the sight always of the white pony, galloping away before them up the next hill beyond, and as steep as it was, she facing up to it as hardy as a goat.

And as for Moira Cloca-dearg, she was in glory !

Not a thought in the world in her only to keep up with the hounds. Faith, she was as proud as that she wouldn't call the King her cousin ! And no blame to her ! Sure she had the boys all left behind, and the white pony under her ready to run to Cork !

Well, above that hill was another one, and it steeper again ! I declare when a person 'd be climbing mountains,

the nearer he'd get to the top, the further off he'd find it !
And that was the way for Moira. When she got above
that hill, she seen before her a big stretch of wet watery
bog, and a kind of an island in the middle of it, and a wide
sort of a fence that divided the bog in two halves, and
crossed out to the island, and follied on from it to the far
side of the bog. And there were all the hounds, and they
not running at all, but going this way and that, and the
smell of the fox lost to them.

Faith the pony wasn't sorry at all to stand still, and
Moira seen that out beyond the bog was hills, going away
away, up into the sky, to further orders, as they say !
Moira looks around for the boys, but deuce a one could
she see.

'O what'll I do now at all ?' says she, and she mad
with the hurry that was in her. 'It must be that blagyard
Fairy Fox we're hunting agin !' says she.

The hounds came up round her and stood there, and
they waving their tails, and looking up at her, and blaming
her for themselves losing the smell.

'Sure I can't help ye, my darlings,' says she to them,
'I d'no no more than yoursels what way is he gone at all !'

With that some o' them lies down and comminces to
roll, and more comminces to scratch, and old Bugler comes
up to the pony's shoulder, and sits down, and looks at
Moira, with his long ears hanging down beside his nose, and

his eyes drooping in his head, like his heart was broke. And Comfort, the little bracket bitch, strays away for herself, and goes wandering around, nosing every place, and getting no satisfaction. Moira was fit to cry ; and not for herself alone, but for the dogs that were waiting on her, and she not able to do a thing for them.

And that now was the minute she heard the horn ! Not Curley Brech's horn at all, but a little fairy horn, no louder than a blackbird's pipe, and it going on strong, blowing 'Gone away !' And then what did she see but two crowds of fairies, and they galloping along out of the little island, on the top of the fence across the bog ! Some o' them was on little weeshy horses, and some only floating in the air, and all colours on them like butterflies ! And then old Bugler rose up and begins to growl, and what was it but the manneen with the red cap beside her !

'Let you not go that way at all !' says he in Irish.

Moira lepped in her saddle.

'And why not ? ' says she, jumping mad to start after the fairies. 'Isn't that the way the fox went ? ' says she. 'Surely I will go !' says she.

'It's no good for ye !' says the manneen.

But there was no holding Moira. She ketches the pony by the head and away with her down to the fence that crossed the bog, and she screeching to the hounds.

'Forrad ! Forrad ! Forrad ! Tally-Ho forrad !'

Well ! The hounds that were so idle and dull, come sweeping on after her like a flood of black water, and the young ones throwing their tongues, and not knowing the reason why at all—the creatures ! Old Bugler and Comfort, the little bracket bitch, weren't running with the rest at all, but going one either side of the pony, and not a word out of them. When Moira comes down to where the fence started to cross the bog, all the pack mounts up on the fence before her, only Bugler and Comfort never stirs, and they stands still before Moira like they wanted to stop her going on the fence.

' What ails ye ? ' says Moira, scolding them. ' Get forrad there ! ' says she. ' 'Ware horse ! ' says she, very angry, riding at them.

They let her pass then, and up on the fence she goes after the hounds that were racing out along it with their heads down, and the cry that they rose then 'd put the heart across in your body ! Away they streams along the top o' the fence, the way the fairies went, and Moira and the white pony after them as clever as one o' them Frenchmen that can walk a rope !

But will ye believe me, half-way across the bog, when Moira got to the little island that was in it, she saw the hounds check, and then, one after the other, she seen them lep out of her sight !

Lusmore, the white pony, stops short.

'What's the matter with ye?' says Moira, mad angry, hitting her a slap with the little *kippen* she had for a whip.

The pony walks on a few steps, and what was there before them but a gap between the island and where the fence continued on, twenty feet and more wide, of deep dark water! When Moira got to it, the most of the hounds was in it, swimming across, and the leaders climbing up on to the fence beyond, and follying on the way the fairies went.

Moira looks at the black water, and she knew then it was the divilment of the fairies that had led her that way, and if it wasn't for the pony being a match for their tricks, she might have galloped into it and never come out of it at all. (Sure bog-holes the like o' that goes down into the next world altogether!)

'It's as good for us to go home,' says she to Lusmore the white pony, and she like to cry, seeing the hounds going from her. She turns around and back with her along the crown o' the fence, and there was old Bugler, and Comfort, the little bracket bitch, sitting waiting for her.

'Show me the way home, good hounds!' says she. Bugler looks up at her, and he growls.

And there was the Cluricaune sitting on a rise o' ground beside her, and he laughing at her!

'Bad luck to them fairies!' says Moira to him, 'putting me astray this way.'

'Why wouldn't ye be said by me?' says the manneen in Irish. 'Go home now,' he says, 'and do as your Mother bid ye.'

He comminces to hammer at the little brogue he was making, and while Moira was looking at him, he soaked away into the hill.

It was only then that Moira thought of the basket she was to take to the Grandmother.

'O murder!' says she, 'Mamma 'll kill me!'

It was well for her Bugler and Comfort was Curley Brech's, and it was for Caherbrech farm they made, and Moira after them, to fetch the basket. Five long Irish miles back in the hills she was; the rain had begun; she put the hood of the Cloca-dearg over her head, and followed on after the two hounds.

The day was closing in when she comes to Caherbrech. Mrs. Wolfe, that was Curley's mother, comes to the door, and Moira asks her for the basket.

'Sure Curley came back from hunting two hours ago,' says Mrs. Wolfe, 'and he said himself 'd run over with the basket to your Grandmother. Come in, girl, out o' the rain, and have a cup o' tea, you're in the want of it, my dear,' says she.

'Thank you, Ma'am,' says Moira, 'I'd be thankful for it, but I must go see my Grandmother, and bring home the basket, or my Mother'll kill me.'

Mrs. Wolfe let Moira go then. Herself and the Grand-mother, that was old Mrs. Dan Sheehan, were for making a match with Moira and Curley, for the farms being convenient that way ; they didn't say a word yet to the girl or the Mother, but Mrs. Wolfe knew well that the boy would be willing, and there was time enough, with them both being as young as they were. But sure women must always be match-making.

When Moira Cloca-dearg got to old Mrs. Dan's house, the half-door was shut.

'I wonder,' says she to herself, 'is she home at all?—But hardly she'd be out in the rain and it so late——'

She gets down off the pony and ties her to the gate of the garden, and knocks at the door of the house.

'The door's not locked at all,' says a wake kind of a voice inside, like a hen that'd have the croup. 'Come in, Asthore, come in why.'

Moira opens the door and goes in.

The kitchen was very dark, but she sees the Grand-mother sitting back in a big old hurlo-thrumbo of a chair that she had, down by the fire. She had a big white cap on her, and a grey shawl over it, and an old quilt over her knees.

'Did ye get the eggs and the butter me Mother sent ye, Grannema?' says Moira.

82

' I did, I did, Asthore,' says the quare voice out o' the chair. ' Come here till I thank ye for them ! '

Moira goes nearer, but she felt frightened like. She looks down into the chair. She sees nothing only the old woman's spectacles shining with the fire in them.

' Why have ye the specs on in the dark like this, Grannema ? ' says she.

' The way I can see you better, Asthore ! ' says the old woman. ' Come here to me, me eyes is dark, I can't see ye at all——'

Moira goes closer. She looks under the big cap and the shawl, and she sees a big mouth, laughing, and it full of white teeth !

' O Grannema ! ' says she. ' When did ye get the grand new set o' teeth and the big red mouth ? ' says she, hardly knowing at all what was she saying for getting worse frightened every minute. (' It's a wicked fairy that's in it, and not Grannema at all ! ' says she to herself.)

' Those are me own teeth, child ; sure I have them always ! ' says the wicked fairy. ' Come here to me and I'll show ye what I have the big mouth for ! '

And with that, Curley the Wolf—for who was it but himself, the blagyard !—leps up out o' the old chair, with the cap and shawl and all falling from him, and he ketches the little girl and kisses her till ye'd think he'd ate the face off her !

'Let me go!' says Moira, trying to loose his arms that were round her. 'What have ye done with me Grandmother?'

Curley Brech holds her tight.

'She's gone to settle with the Priest,' says he. 'There's time yet! This is the last day of Shraft, and I'll wait no longer,' says he. 'We'll be married to-night!' says he.

. . . .

And so they were too, and if ye'll believe me, the little Cluricaune was before them, and they coming out of the Chapel, and he threw a little shoe after them that ye wouldn't get the like of in the whole world, no, nor in the globe of Ireland neither.

VIII

A BETRAYAL OF CONFIDENCE

TO be an aunt is, for some obscure reason, to become a target for the slings and arrows of outrageous comic papers. Why the fact that brothers or sisters have seen fit to obey the command to replenish the earth should react unfavourably upon their female relatives it is hard to say. Yet it is indisputable that the aunt, and especially a spinster of the species, is made the victim of circumstances over which she has, obviously, no control.

Miss Elizabeth Dawson was an aunt, even a rich aunt— a being who, it is generally assumed, can only justify her existence by leaving it with all speed—and she did her best to gratify such conventional expectations, by indulging in a passion for hunting the fox that was considered by her family to be not only dangerous and expensive, but ridiculous. She read Beckford, and Vyner, and Radcliffe to the bone; she could repeat long passages from *Handley Cross* from memory; her collections of hunting classics and coloured prints were as complete as money could make them, and, in the opinion of her four married sisters, she spent upon horses far more than any single woman (with a considerable number of nieces and nephews) was justified in doing.

The four married sisters were in the habit of saying that Really, Elizabeth, at her age . . . (but this, since Elizabeth was the youngest of the family, they did not specify). And the four brothers-in-law, none of whom had ever ridden, or even wanted to ride, became, when Elizabeth's infatuation was discussed, almost too angry to be sarcastic.

One only of the sisterhood of six had never commented on the unsuitability of Elizabeth's recreations—(it should be added that she spent her summers in playing Lawn Tennis) —but that, possibly, was because this sister had been so misguided as to have married an Irishman and lived in Ireland, where all women are girls until they marry. Alas, she had died before Elizabeth had attained to the humiliating age of fifty-five.

It was at about the time when this misfortune (which is, after all, common to many) had overtaken Miss Dawson, that she began to realize another and almost more painful fact, that her horses had grown old more rapidly than she, and that what had been good hunters had now entered the category of crocks. It was apparent to her that, if she did not wish to lose the season—it was already November, and at her age she was aware of the danger of breaking a link in the chain of sport—something drastic had to be done. And, as it happened, just at this juncture came to her a letter from her nephew, Charles Waller, who was the son of that misguided lady who had been buried, at first socially, subsequently in a less figurative sense, in Ireland.

MY DEAR AUNT,—[Charles wrote] Why wouldn't you come over and have a hunt here? There is a nice foxy mare I know that would suit you. The Regiment that's here now are very decent chaps. They come out with me and give me a good subscription. The Col's name is Medway. He is a cross old devil but I'll say for him he goes well and so does his daughter.

'Medway?' thought Elizabeth. 'Can it possibly be Tommy Medway?'

The gliding phrases of the 'Blue Danube' sang them- selves in her mind, linked with a vision of a slim youth in a scarlet mess jacket. She thought 'A cross old devil! Perhaps I'm well out of him after all!'

Yet, though the thought of the foxy mare was upper- most, she admitted to herself that it would be amusing to meet Tommy Medway again.

So she bestowed one of her crocks upon a niece, and another upon a farmer, and a third (with a tear or two) she sent to the Kennels, and announced to her friends that she was going to Ireland to buy horses.

To her disapproving sisters she said :

'I shall stay with Charles.'

7   87

And this, if possible, made things worse, since Charles was to his other aunts an unknown quantity that might develop into a menace to its co-nephews.

Miss Dawson, alone of the sisterhood, had been accustomed to face the perils that are believed to beset those who dare three hours of St. George's Channel, and she had stayed with her exiled sister, Mrs. Waller, often enough to be able to boast that she knew Ireland and liked it. This was, indeed, rather less than the facts of the case, since opposition had fostered in the ingenuous Elizabeth that enthusiasm for all things Irish which is frequently met with in the visitor to Erin (and but seldom in the native). This generous passion had taken the young man, Charles, as its central point, a fact that to Charles's other aunts, each of whom possessed incomparable sons, was legitimately trying.

Charles, so far from being incomparable, was a plain youth with a brogue, a good seat on a horse, and a noted incapacity for making his income correspond with what he held to be his necessities. But his Aunt Elizabeth, though old enough (as her sisters said) to know better, condoned the imperfections of Charles, and supplemented his income in order that one of his leading necessities, which was a small pack of foxhounds, might be kept as they should be. She furnished him with nearly as perfect an assortment of Works on Hunting as her own, and believed that he studied them and laid their precepts to heart as assiduously as she did ; not realizing the fact that the humbler the Hunt the more convinced are its Master and its Members that they have nothing to learn from any one.

. . . .

' No,' said Elizabeth Dawson, addressing the driver of the outside-car with the firmness of the travelled English-woman who knows she knows her Ireland, ' not another penny ! I am already giving you a shilling more than your proper fare.'

The response of the car-driver was to the effect that he would die down dead on the road before he would be deprived of his rights by one that was no lady, and he endorsed this decision (which he appeared to regard as a threat) by snatching Miss Dawson's dressing-box and replac-ing it upon his car. At this juncture Miss Dawson's porter, who had preserved, as is invariable in such affrays, a strict neutrality during the contest, suggested, deferentially, that the guard had his flag wove and the train was for starting. Recognizing *force majeure*, Elizabeth yielded the position and the shilling in dispute, adding that she would take care never to employ the extortioner again.

' My darlin' child,' replied the car-driver, with a sweet-ness for which his previous manner had not prepared his fare, pocketing the shilling, and restoring the dressing-box to the porter, ' whenever I see ye, I'll avoid ye! '

'I'm *not* your darling child!' Miss Dawson shouted angrily over her shoulder, as she rushed after the porter. But she knew that though she might have had the last word, victory was to the car-driver.

On her arrival that evening at her journey's end, Elizabeth was immediately conscious of raised temperatures and strain in all departments.

She was met at the station in heavy rain, by the Second Whip, with a pony-trap, and the news that there was to be a by-day to-morrow, and the Master couldn't come for her, as himself and John Casey was away about stopping.

'The Meet's at the Kennels,' he added, 'and I'm told there's high quality expected. I'm painting the Kennel railings and cutting nettles all day.'

Miss Dawson had had sufficient experience of the conditions of her nephew's establishment to know that these duties, not usually allied with that of Whipper-in, might, none the less, come within his sphere of action ; but when, in the hall, she encountered the cook cleaning the Master's white leather breeches, and the parlourmaid met her on the stairs and showed her to her bedroom with a buttonstick in her hand and a red coat over her arm, she recognized that this was a very exceptional by-day, and was glad that she had brought her new habit.

Charles, when, near dinner-time, he came home, exhibited a nerve tension unusual in him.

'MY DARLIN' CHILD, WHENEVER I SEE YE, I'LL AVOID YE!

' I'm half dead and I'm wet through, and I don't believe there's a dam' fox in the country!' he said, stabbing savagely at a sulky turf fire in the drawing-room with a poker like a stiletto.

' Then why have a by-day?' inquired his aunt, not unreasonably.

Her nephew got red, and hesitated a little.

' Well, it was rather a special thing—a word I got from —from the Barracks, that the General was come to inspect, and he was mad keen for hunting—and she said—I mean the Colonel said—wouldn't I make a by-day for him. You see—' Charles hung fire for a moment, ' Miss Medway, that's the Colonel's daughter, says the Colonel would like to please the General—jolly him with a bit of a hunt, y'know —and—' Charles paused again and kicked a red setter out of the middle of the hearth-rug, ' it'd be no harm for me to please the Colonel——'

In the idiom of the south of Ireland under-statement is generally a form of intensification. (' But why—' thought Elizabeth, ' why is Charles so anxious to please Tommy Medway?')

' All I'm afraid of,' Charles continued, ' is about finding a fox. There've been some blackguard rabbit-trappers about. Me and John Casey were round warning the chaps that stop for me. The half of them won't leave their beds till the foxes are underground, and then they stop them in!

They tell me there's a certain-sure fox in Hurley's Wood—
but very likely that's a lie. I'll try it first anyway. I saw
John Casey's brother too——' Charles looked sideways at
his aunt. 'You might remember the bit of covert there is
on the hill there? His boys say there's a fox there all
right—but *I* dunno! It's going to be the devil of a wet
night. I suppose we'll have a blank day!' He laughed
bitterly, as one versed in the malevolence of Providence.
'By George! I'd turn down a bag-man fast enough if I
had one—or—or run a drag!'

'My dear boy!' exclaimed Elizabeth, horrified, 'I'm
sure you can't really mean that! Don't you remember
what Vyner says about what he calls "the cocktail and
unmanly amusement of bag-fox-hunting"? And as for a
drag! Oh! Worse still!'

'What have cocktails got to do with it?' demanded
Charles, defiantly. 'That's all rot! By the Holy Fly!
I'd run a drag for tuppence if I could make sure the Colonel
wouldn't spot it! He's as full up with rules out of books
as yourself, Aunt! Well, I must get out of these wet
things——' At the door he turned. 'I'll bet there'll be
one out who'd like a gallop, drag or no!'

He shut the door with a bang.

Elizabeth said to herself: 'And *I'll* bet there's a young
woman at the bottom of all this!'

The ensuing night justified Charles's pessimism. John

Casey, who was Kennel Huntsman and First Whip, appeared at the dining-room door while breakfast was in progress and said he didn't see the like o' the rain last night since the day he was born, adding that the day didn't look too good at all, and there was a mountain of water outside in the lawn.

'I suppose we'll not find at all, so,' Charles responded gloomily, accepting the phenomenon without surprise.

'Unless it'd be at me brother's,' said John Casey, quickly. 'The mare's here for you, Miss,' he went on. 'They're fitting your saddle on her now.'

'I hope she's up to my weight,' said Elizabeth, who walked a good eleven stone.

John Casey looked her up and down.

'It's all I fear, Miss, ye're not weighty enough to steady her! It's a snaffle they have on her. You might be hard set to hold her in a snaffle. Sure that's a powerful young mare that'd tear a house after her! Will I tell them put a double bridle on her?'

'I'll ride her in whatever she's used to,' said Miss Dawson, firmly, although the enconium on the mare's abilities was disquieting.

The meet on the road outside the Kennels was select and impressive. The regiment had justified Charles's opinion of its decency by turning out in strength, and the neighbourhood had supplied its highest quality to do honour to the

General. That officer and the Colonel were the centre of
a respectful group of local riders, who were capping each
other's anecdotes of the achievements of the pack. The
Master, a little withdrawn from the throng, was talking to
a young lady on a big brown horse, and the Hounds had
but just appeared upon the scene when Miss Dawson, on
the foxy mare, arrived.

Elizabeth's start had not been without its difficulties.
The mare, a large young lady, four years of age, sixteen-two
hands high, well able to carry fifteen stone, with flickering
ears and a glancing eye, had declined to be manœuvred
alongside the chair that had been intended as a mounting-
block, and Miss Dawson had therefore been compelled to
accompany her for some time about the yard, hopping on
her right foot, in collaboration with the stable-boy, whose
grasp of her left foot threatened to dislocate her hip joint,
and was quite unrelated to the act of raising her to the
saddle.

Now, as at a headstrong trot she joined the crowd on the
road by the Kennels, her rider was beginning to wonder
if it were not true that she might be hard-set to hold her
in a snaffle, but with the General on one hand, being gallant
(as becomes a General), and the Colonel—who was indeed
Tommy Medway—being sentimentally reminiscent (as becomes a friend of other days) on the other, Miss Dawson
put regretful thoughts of a good heavy double bridle away.

The General was in a mood of sunny approval of every-thing. That was a fine chestnut Miss Dawson was on ! And it was a pleasure to see a lady riding *like* a lady—not this modern straddle-saddle business, which was poison to him ! And the Hounds looked a nice sharp, workmanlike lot ! Not one of these bobbery packs that will run anything from a bag-man to a red herring !

' I can answer for it that Miss Dawson's nephew's hounds are the right sort ! ' put in the Colonel, archly ; ' I've seen Mr. Waller's library ! All the classics there, and I know who gave them to him ! '

No tribute could have pleased Elizabeth more. She and the two warriors were proceeding to discuss, with enjoyable disapproval, various forms of illegitimate sport, when the Hounds moved off, and to check the foxy mare's resolve to move in their midst, so absorbed her attention that the denunciations of her companions became indistinguishably blended for her with the simultaneous indignation of two cur-dogs in the yard of a neighbouring farm.

The Hounds soon left the road, and Charles and his men trotted with them across a couple of fields to a long wood. A thin rain had begun to fall, and a cold south-east wind gave it penetrating power, but Miss Dawson was too fully occupied to be more than subconsciously aware of such matters. Had the wet green pasture-field been paved with red-hot flags, her mount could hardly have improved on her method of dealing with the difficulty. Lawn tennis and golf had done their part in keeping Elizabeth's muscles in good repair, but having been taken across the field in a series of irregular frog-springs, in each of which was the thought, not quite matured, of a buck, and through a narrow gateway like a shot out of a gun, she took advantage of the position at the tails of the Hounds that was forced upon her, to humble herself to John Casey, and admit the inadequacy of the snaffle.

John Casey had a wild eye and a hurried manner. 'Wait, for God's sake, Miss, till we have the wood drawn, and if we don't find, I'll slip this martingale that I have meself on to her——'

He struck in his spurs, and his horse started off at a gallop, as is the hard-learnt habit of a Whip's horse.

A prolonged wait followed. Elizabeth found the girl on the brown horse beside her and fell into conversation. Yes, the girl liked hunting. Was only a beginner. Mr. Waller was so kind to strangers, he had taught her quite a lot already. How provoking this rain was ! Her father had told her to go home, but she didn't think she was going ! With which she turned the brown horse and moved to the rear.

There was no fox in the wood. It became known to the Field that the Hounds had gone on to a plantation three miles away, and a dreary jog along a rough road followed.

The riders were herded into a field in the eye of the wind and rain, the Hounds were swallowed up by the wood, and all was still. After what felt like a lifetime, Elizabeth found John Casey beside her, but his promised aid was still withheld.

' Sure I can't yet, Miss— The Devil's very busy with Master Charles to-day ! He's black mad we can't find a fox. He'll try the bog below now, and I must surround it —after that, maybe——'

He sped away, and Elizabeth began to think seriously of going home, while the foxy mare, stirred by the incident, got her back up, and bucked very efficiently three times.

At this moment Miss Dawson was again joined by her martial friends, and their warmly expressed advice to her to stay out no longer, enforced by disapproval of her mount, roused her to opposition.

' She'll settle down soon,' she said, repressing with difficulty the mare's furious pawing at the ground in the manner of an angry bull. ' These waits are rather trying—she's cold and cross—like me ! '

' No, no ! ' protested the Colonel, regarding Elizabeth, whose looks had withstood the attrition of time with considerable success, with the eye attributed by Shakespeare to soldiers, ' you mustn't say that ! In those times that *you* may have forgotten, but I have not, I have known you cold, but never cross ! '

Miss Dawson did not feel in the mood to respond in a suitable key, but she was spared the necessity of trying to do so by far-off touches of the horn, telling of another failure followed by a distant sight of the Master and the Hounds moving off at a fast trot. The Field burst into life and pursuit, Elizabeth, much against her own wish, ramping in the van. Presently she found John Casey beside her.

'He's going to try me brother's hill, Miss,' he said, hurriedly. 'Let you come on quick with me, and I'll give you this martingale——'

They were in a narrow lane, stony and wet as the bed of a stream. Elizabeth was far in advance of the other riders, and she now gave the mare her head and galloped, splashing and clattering, in John Casey's wake, and soon found herself in a farmyard. Her guide was already on foot, talking eagerly to a couple of youths, while he took the martingale off his horse.

'Take the bed from under her, the way I told ye——' he was saying quickly, as Miss Dawson reined in beside him.

The youths vanished into a stable, and John Casey hurried on with his task.

'Isn't it a murder the foxes to be under ground this way, Miss? And this day above all, with the General out, and Master Charles as cross as briars! But sure the hill here is a fright for holding foxes! Too many there is in it always!

99

To be sure there was some lads trapping rabbits lately—
me nephews here got a vixen in it and a trap hanging to
her—— But there's more in it than herself ! Stand, mare,
will ye ! Now, Miss ! That'll put the fear o' God in her ! '

As Elizabeth rode out of the yard she met Miss Medway.

' What ? Not gone ? '

' Only going,' replied Miss Medway, apologetically. ' I
—I met the Master, and he said I ought to give the day
another chance—he was going to draw some covert near
here——'

This, however, the day did not seem inclined to take.
Miss Medway went away. A quarter of an hour passed in
dripping silence. The foxy mare tore mouthfuls of grass
from the fence opposite the farmyard gate. Miss Dawson
pensively consumed her sandwiches, with the feeling of
being profoundly remote from all earthly things that such
moments engender.

Suddenly round a turn of the road Charles came riding
fast towards her, with the Hounds, muddy and dispirited,
splashing after him.

' Aunt ! Did you see John Casey ? ' he shouted, dragging his horse to a stand, ' and Miss Medway ? Wasn't she
here ? I told John Casey I'd meet him here—where the
devil the fellow's gone I dunno ! He's never in the place
I want him ! ' He stood up in his stirrups, staring all
round. ' I've drawn every blasted covert in the country !

Not a smell of a fox in any one o' them—they can't say I haven't tried !'

Before Elizabeth could speak, the missing John Casey, his face as red as his coat, came galloping up to them.

'It's all right, Master Charles ! Bring them on, Sir ! Bring them on !' Then he noticed Master Charles's aunt, and his voice's peculiar tone, at once confidential and triumphant, changed to a more official key. 'There's a fox, gone away out of the hill above, Master ! A boy's just after seeing him go !'

Electric light could not blaze more instantly and responsively than did Charles and his Hounds to this intelligence. In a single thrilling second all were away, racing up the narrow farm lane, whirling round the end of a farm building, Charles's horn going, John Casey's whip cracking. A moment later Elizabeth saw them half-way up the rough hill-side above the farm.

The foxy mare stood up on her hind legs twice, in expression of emotion, and then the splashing rattle of hoofs in the stony lane behind her warned her to waste no more time, so also did Miss Dawson's crop, with a solid thump on her big flank, and she fled up the lane after the Hunt, with the surging crowd of riders coming racing to the horn, hard on her heels.

Over a low wall, up the hill by a zigzag cart-track, then over a broad heather-covered bank went Miss Dawson and

the foxy mare, the cry of the Hounds now added to the
doubling of Charles's horn. Beyond the bank the country
lay open before her, sloping downwards in wide pasture-
fields, and three big fields ahead of her went the Hounds,
with their Huntsman close to them, legging it down the
hill, their rejoicing voices streaming back to their followers.
Elizabeth found the brown horse beside her.

'What luck !' gasped his rider. 'Thought I should never
catch you !'

The General and the Colonel were close behind, the rest
of the Field spreading in a fan behind them. Miss Dawson's
full strength, abetted by John Casey's martingale, was
needed to keep her mount's enthusiasm within bounds.
This is, indeed, no figure of speech in connexion with the
foxy mare's method of progression, which suggested that of
a super-kangaroo. Bank after bank she flung behind her,
gaining speed as she went. She was into the field next
behind the flying Hounds now, sweeping over a rough stone
wall in her mighty stride. Elizabeth, tough and experienced
as she was, was beginning to wonder how much more pulling
her arms would stand, when she saw, with relief, Charles
hold up his hand and stop his horse. The Hounds had
checked at a lane. They were cast ahead, without result ;
then Charles galloped with them up and down the lane,
with no better success.

'Thundering good fox, this !' puffed the General, rather

blown, but in high spirits. ' Funny their losing him so suddenly ! One would have said they were tied to him ! '

The Colonel came up, looking black.

' I've sent Mollie home. She's ridden that horse to a standstill. He's done—cooked ! She's no judgement ! Very strange no one seems to have viewed this fox—funny sort of a find ! You'd have thought the feller that viewed him away would have hollered——' He looked hard at Miss Dawson. ' One o' these farmers here was sniggering——'

Elizabeth fired up.

' Are you suggesting it's a *drag*, Colonel Medway ? ' she demanded, hotly. ' I may assure you that *my* nephew——'

But the defence could go no further. At a remote corner of the field in which they were standing, a hound spoke ; in an instant his comrades had joined him and the Master's horn told that the run was still alive and a going concern.

What followed was brief, but was made memorable by the overthrow of the Colonel, which occurred at a very high bank with a ditch on the landing side. The disaster was made more acute by the fact that Miss Dawson, coming up behind at the headlong rate of speed dictated by the foxy mare, was unaware of what had happened, until, poised for a moment on the summit of the bank, she saw a bald head in the ditch immediately below her. To whom it belonged she neither knew nor cared, her single anxiety being to

8   103

clear it. Therefore, since, with horror, she realized that the owner of the head was beginning to struggle out of the ditch on to the spot where she must inevitably alight, she shrieked : 'Lie down, you fool !' and gave the mare so vigorous a clout with her crop, that she sailed in a rainbow curve far out into the field, thus saving Colonel Medway's life, and implanting in him an eternal rancour, for to be called a fool, and jumped over, by a former flame (of fifty-five if she was a day) is the sort of thing no self-respecting gentleman can be expected to stand.

The run, however, lasted but a few minutes longer. The Colonel's horse was caught and remounted, and he, the General, Elizabeth, and John Casey, with Charles a little ahead, were riding neck and neck along a road when the Hounds again checked. A scarlet-faced, perspiring lad was leaning against a gate-post, and Charles yelled at him the usual inquiry :

'Did ye see the fox ?'

'I did, I did !' the lad answered, with a shout of laughter. 'Isn't he just after giving me his coat to hold ?'

Charles, made reckless by discovery, began to laugh wildly. What the Colonel, his face plastered with mud, said, need not be repeated. The General forgot his principles in the glow of the gallop, and said he didn't care a damn if the fox had two legs or four, he had given them a damn good twenty minutes. The stricken aunt of the criminal was too shattered by shock to speak, or even to realize that Miss Medway, who had mysteriously rejoined the first flight, was gazing at her guilty nephew with eyes that shone with admiration, and was murmuring, ' It was all *too* marvellous ! '

John Casey, alone, addressed the fox's faithless confederate in suitable terms.

' Ye're me own brother's son, Jerry Casey, and it's all I wish that the Divil may sweep hell with ye and burn the broom after ! '

IX

'NOT THE WOMAN'S PLACE'

TIME was when there were but few forms of healthy, normal enjoyment to which these words, pregnant of prunes, prisms, and prisons, did not apply. Regarding the matter dispassionately, by the light of literature as well as that of social history, it would seem that the sole places on God's pleasant earth to which this warning placard was not affixed were those wherein The Woman was occupied with her dealings with the other sex ; directly, as in the ball-room, or indirectly, as in the nursery. The indoor traditions of the harem governed the diversions and relaxations of the early Victorian ladies. The few exceptions proved—to quote for the thousandth time the age-worn aphorism—a rule that did not indeed need any proving, being unquestioned.

Let us consider, for example, the matter of Hunting, with which I propose more especially to deal. There was

A BITTER NORTH-WEST WIND, SNOW-LADEN AND FIERCE

in England, in the eighteenth century, a Marchioness of
Salisbury, who kept and followed the Hertfordshire Hounds ;
in Ireland, at about the same period, there was a Countess
of Bandon of high renown as a rider. In literature there
was ' Diana Vernon', who is spoken of with awe as having
' guided her horse with the most admirable address and
presence of mind ', and even ' cleared an obstruction composed of forest timber at a flying leap'. Later, Surtees,
and Whyte Melville, and John Leech evolved between them
a few beings who qualified their prowess in floating over
five-barred gates by suitable attacks of faintness during
emotional crises ; but these were all exceptions. In other
sports—shooting, rowing, boat-sailing—the rule required no
proving, which was fortunate, as I think there were no
exceptions. In art, a tepid water-colour or so was tolerated ;
elegant volumes of ' Keepsakes ' received the overflowings of
the feminine literary fount in contributions that ran smoothly
in the twin channels of knightly heroism and female fidelity,
varied perhaps by a dirge for a departed ring-dove or a sob
for a faded rosebud.

Even in philanthropy, in whose domain the conventional
Ministering Angel might have been assigned a place, ' The
Woman ' was assured that she had none. I have been
privileged to meet one of Miss Florence Nightingale's con-
temporaries and acquaintances, an old lady of over ninety,
with whom to speak was as though one had leaped back-

wards through the rushing years and landed in a peaceful backwater of earliest Victorian times.

'Florence Nightingale?' said this little old lady, buried in a big chair, looking like a tiny, shrivelled white mouse with bright blue eyes and grey mittens. 'Ah! yes, I knew her well. A beautiful woman, my dear; but she had that curious fancy for washing dirty men!'—which, no doubt, expressed a very general view of the life-work of the Lady with the Lamp.

Probably when the history is written of how The Woman's place in the world came to include 'All out-doors' (as they say in America), as well as what has been called in Ireland, 'the work that is within', it will be acknowledged that sport, Lawn Tennis, Bicycling, and Hunting, played quite as potent a part as education in the emancipation that has culminated in the Representation of the People Bill. The playing-fields of Eton did not as surely win Waterloo as the hunting-fields and lawn-tennis grounds of the kingdom won the vote for women.

In no region of sport has freedom 'broadened down' with greater rapidity than in hunting. Of hunting, on the whole, it must be said that 'Convention's casket holds her sacred things'. The red-tape of tradition has long bound her hand and foot, until, say, the last five-and-twenty or thirty years, the proper place of woman in regard to the foxhunter has been laid down in the verse of the old hunting-song:

The wife around her husband throws
Her arms to make him stay.
' My dear, it rains, it hails, it blows !
My dear (*crescendo*), it rains, it *hails*, it BLOWS !
You cannot hunt to-day, you cannot hunt to-day ! '

(wherein the wife, if right about the weather, was very probably right also about the hunting ; and while, still in bed, she comfortably drinks her ' early tea ', the husband, with his collar up to his ears and his back to a hedge, is asking himself why he had been ass enough to think there was a fox above ground on such a morning. This, however, is not the point, which is sufficiently obvious).

It was pretty late in the nineteenth century, taking the unerring pages of *Punch* as a guide, before women were tolerated (later still before they were welcomed) in the hunting field, a fact for which I find it hard to blame the then masters of the situation. In those early times women were obsessed (one gathers it again from *Punch*) with the need of making themselves agreeable, which frequently meant that they talked at the wrong moments and too much. (I am not saying that this practice is entirely a matter of the past.) If a woman's horse fell, she was probably more hurt than a man would be ; in any case, her horse had to be caught, and some one had to mount her, which gave almost as much trouble as if she had been killed (I was going to have said without the attendant compensation, but refrain). Those early pictures set forth unsparingly the various feminine foibles. The lady who talks the fox back into covert, who holds up the hunt while she fumbles at a gate, whose horse invariably kicks hounds, or anything else that is near enough ; even that unfortunate lady to whom a man has to devote his coat because her horse and habit skirt have followed the Hounds without her. Improvement in these matters was gradual, but it came. The modern side-saddle did much ; the introduction of safety-aprons did more, riding astride will probably do most of all. Di Vernon was, no doubt, seated on a species of howdah with a well-like centre, her right leg enclosed by two in-curving crutches, her left foot resting in a contrivance like a fossilized bedroom slipper. Miss Lucy Glitters and Kate Coventry wore habits that might, at a pinch, have enclosed a crinoline.

The safety-apron has possibly seen its most brilliant days, and the ride-astride outfit is fast superseding all others. Many, and beyond telling, are its advantages, yet, at the risk of incurring the contempt of those whose opinion counts for most, and is least worth having (I allude to the rising generation), I would like to say that the basis of good hands is a firm seat, and this, in conjunction with a ride-astride outfit, is unusual.

My own earliest recollection of hunting belongs to those prehistoric times when Man went forth to the chase, and

Woman, at best, palpitated over her lord's prowess from the vantage-point of the family outside-car, possibly even, if the day were inclement and the scene the County Cork, from the purdah-like depths of the family inside-car, or jingle. My first remembered day with Hounds was, however, a remarkable variant of the accepted rule, and is, for that reason, worthy of record. A bagged fox was to be 'shaken', and to me, unworthy member of the unworthier sex, befell the pony (whose age, sixteen, just doubled mine), while my brother, of somewhat tenderer years, it is true, drove to the meet upon an outside-car, in tears and a black spotted net veil. The veil was enforced by the nursery authority, in deference to a 'stye' in his eye; the tears were the natural result of this outrage upon masculine dignity. It is recorded that the little boy, still, like a heroine of old romance, weeping and closely veiled, held a corner of the bag during the ceremony of releasing the fox from it, but this alleviation was entirely outweighed by the fact that his sister, for reasons not specially apparent, was subsequently given the brush, and bore it back to the nursery in offensive triumph.

It is because of its remarkable foreshadowing of the future that the incident has been rescued from oblivion. It is now the girl of the family who rides to hounds, seriously and consistently, and, when her brothers return for the Christmas holidays, gravely debates with the groom as to whether the pony will be 'too much for the young gentle-men'.   It is melancholy to relate that the young gentlemen are, as often as not, singularly unselfish in the matter of the pony, and are more especially so when a day's shooting is the alternative.   The heart of the Flapper is as yet untainted by the rival attraction of the gun, and, so remarkable has been the progress of emancipation, I have even known of hunting governesses who took the field with their charges and were the envy and admiration of those parents not possessed of so undaunted a deputy.

I have seen an old book on hunting which, in advocating the presence of the Fair Sex at a meet, offered, apologetically, the reason that such an intrusion would enable them 'to exhibit becoming costumes, and would fit them to talk agreeably and with intelligence to the gentlemen after dinner'.   That was in 1830, or thereabouts ; more than a century ago, and a century that has, perhaps, done more to turn the world upside down than any of its predecessors.

Inevitably, as one ponders upon the changed locale of 'the woman's place', the stupendous revolution brought about by the War comes to mind.   Sports, as sports, have temporarily gone under.   The muscle, the nerve, the vitality that they bred in women have been applied in other spheres, and in many munition works and hospitals have proved their value.

Hunting, alone among sports, serves a positive national

need. At the beginning of the War it is no exaggeration to say that the Hunts saved the situation as far as the cavalry was concerned, and the Army, while it demanded the men and horses that hunting had created, and by whom hunting lived, moved, and had its being, illogically insisted that Hounds must be kept going and that cavalry remounts must not fail. Thus it came about that ' the woman's place ', as often as not, was necessarily the stables, and lady-masters and lady-grooms laid the axe to the root of a long-cherished monopoly. Not one, but many Hunts must, during the bad years, have gone under, were it not that their Masters' wives and daughters, instead of throwing their arms round their men ' to bid them stay ', as laid down by the song, strengthened their hearts to go, and without considering whether it rained, hailed, or blew, took over the Hounds and what were left of the horses, and ' carried on '.

I have in mind a Hunt in an Irish county, in which, what time the bugle blew the advance, the Master ' dug out ' himself and such of his staff as were eligible, leaving the Hunt in the hands of his wife, uncertain of all things save the way his duty lay. His wife stood up to the situation, as a good sportswoman will. She ' carried on ', she even ' carried the horn ' and hunted the Hounds herself, afraid of one thing only, that when the Master came home he would say that she had spoilt the Hounds. (It may here be stated that no such calamity occurred ; the end of the War found the morals of the pack unimpaired.)

Only such as battled through those first bad days can at all realize what was involved in the game of carrying on. The wearing strain of the commissariat alone, bad enough in pre-war days, was enough to overwhelm the novice. Flesh, meal, biscuits, having doubled in price, withdrew themselves from the public view, and waited, in cloistered calm, until dearth had prepared those that needed them for extortions such as exceeded their darkest anticipations. And this was not the only strain.

The popular view of foxhunting, largely based on Christmas numbers and their like, is sometimes justified, and ' the gay throng that goes laughing along ', exclusively composed of young and beautiful riders and horses, a flawless pack of identical hounds, a fox who is shot from the covert as from a pop-gun at the psychological moment, have, no doubt, occasionally occurred—' the time and the place and the loved one all together ', as it were. The usual hunting record is dedicated to success, the glories and ecstasies of foxhunting need not here be sung. I should like to write the story of a hunting day more typical of the past time of war, and to show faithfully, if faintly, what were some of the minor trials of a Deputy Master, and, as Ireland is best known to me, let that day be in Ireland. (There is no need to say that the facts apply to no special

Hunt, since, given the position, they were practically common to all.)

Our typical day for our typical Deputy begins, probably, at some eight of the clock, when a message, poisoning the first and most precious moments of the day, is delivered from the Kennels, to say, idiomatically, that 'it made a frost early in the night, but the thaw was begun, and will the Hounds be to go out?'

Peace ceases for the Deputy Master. She puts on her dressing-gown and visits, with groanings, 'the glass'. It is falling, which probably means snow. An icy blast from an open window (windows should be sealed, she decides, in a north-westerly winter wind) suggests an impending blizzard. 'Take not out your hounds on a windy day'; she remembers Beckford's counsel, and longs to have courage to obey him. But the meet is advertised. The conscience of a good young Deputy Master is a very tender thing; there is moreover something attractive in the knotted scourge and the hair shirt to the zealot.

'Tell him "Yes, if the horses can travel,"' she says firmly.

She feels reasonably certain that there will be no hunting. The governess is away and the children have colds: she has Red Cross work to do, and her unanswered letters face her as Banquo's murdered line faced Macbeth. But advertised fixtures are solemn things, especially to a Deputy

Master; she gloomily gets into her habit. The post is no later than was usual in those days of war; it arrives in time to embitter her last moments, already made poignant by demands and inquiries from all and sundry of those over whom she has been set in authority (a meaningless phrase, that should be directly reversed where the ruler of an Irish country establishment is concerned).

Motors, it is needless to say, do not at this period exist; and the meet is nine miles away. The Deputy Master meets the Hounds and the elderly Whipper-in at her own gate. Her mare is fresh, the road is slippery, the Hounds are demonstrative in their affection. For a moment she confidently expects to find herself and the mare on their backs in the gutter. 'Wilful', the spoilt puppy whom she herself had walked, having first, to the fury of the mare, clawed, with tom-cat-like mollrowings of affection, that lady's shining shoulder, then proceeds to get under her feet, to the acute peril of all concerned. A bitter north-west wind, snow-laden and fierce, fights every inch of advance along the road to the meet. Our Master's hands go dead; the Hounds' jog, at which she must perforce travel, does not conduce to raising the temperature, and the mare's exuber-ance of spirits, which becomes more pronounced where the frost under the surface slime is most slippery, does not find a response in her rider's breast.

She arrives early at the meet, a bleak cross-roads near

a long wood. The Earth-stopper only is there, an old man, versed in guile, steeped in lies.

'Ere midnight I shut every hole o' them, my lady,' he says. 'Oh! divil a beetle could get in or out o' them!' And again: 'Oh! full o' foxes it is! Didn't one whip seven laying pullets from me wife a' Sunday night?'

The Master ignores the conundrum; she sees, scudding towards her across the fields, two women, and knows too well their mission. (Have I said that she is also manager of the Fowl Fund? She is)—and a good number of that ringing company of half-crowns with which she daily stuffs her hunting-purse have left it for ever, before the iniquities of the foxes are all recited and the Field arrives. The Field (that 'glad throng that goes laughing along') consists of the Hon. Sec., who is a woman impervious to weather, faithful more than most, and a little boy on a bare-backed pony, who wears winkers that do not conceal the hatred for the Hounds that gleams in his eyes.

'Take that pony out of that!' commands the Master.

The little boy obeys with *empressement*, but as he retires through the centre of the pack, the pony gets in at least one kick before it is too late.

'I believe Mrs. Dash is coming,' says the Hon. Sec.; 'I met her at the War-work, and she said if her horse wasn't wanted to plough—she's begun her extra tillage, you know—

she was coming out. You might give her a little law, she's always rather late, and Hennessy told me he'd be out——' (Hennessy is a farmer, mildly sporting, and much courted in consequence by the Hon. Sec., with whom such birds are precious as they are rare.)

A hail-shower, which might have been fired by a machine-gun, comes swishing over the hills above the covert, and decides the question of further ' law ' for the always rather late Mrs. Dash, or even for the courted Hennessy. The Deputy Master, with lips stiff with cold, ' touches ' her horn (a recent and imperfectly acquired accomplishment) and elicits a note that is not specially cheering, being suggestive of an abortive attempt upon a pocket-handkerchief; it suffices, however, for the shivering Hounds, and the ' glad throng ' moves on into the wood.

Too well, on such a day as this, does the Master know the ways of X—— Wood. Along a cart-track deep in sticky black mire, she moves slowly, encouraging the Hounds, who are invisible in the thick undergrowth of the wood. She is not well versed in ' hound language ', and trusts the Hon. Sec. is out of hearing, but she does her best to keep things lively, despite the *silence morne et vaste* of the Hounds. The central ride accomplished, the narrow tracks, cut for woodcock-shooters through the close-growing, stunted myriads of oaks, hollies, and ashes, have to be dealt with. The sleet-showers have less power to harm, but the going is worse, and the peril from overhanging branches more acute. The Earth-stopper materializes mysteriously at intervals with specious encouragement.

'Thry south, Ma'am ! Oh, surely he's in it ! There's tin o' them in it ! There was a woman picking sticks and didn't she say he faced herself and the little dog she had, to bite them !'

The Master tries south, also north, east, and west. The older and wiser Hounds string out at her heels, along the narrow ride. They have ascertained that there are no foxes and no scent. They listen to the squeals of Wilful, who is now hunting rabbits, with expressions that would befit Elders of the Scotch Kirk were brawling to take place during service.

The Deputy Master is reasonably certain that the foxes have been 'stopped in ', still it is her duty to try out the wood and she does it. The younger Hounds have followed Wilful to do evil, and are indemnifying themselves for the absence of scent and foxes by running rabbits at view. The Master rates them in vain. They know her best as an over-indulgent purveyor of biscuit and minor delicacies ; the elderly Whipper-in is far away, outside the covert, on the lee-side of a fence, cursing the weather, the Earth-stopper, and the foxes, with the lurid misanthropy of a minor prophet.

The wood and its surroundings have been ' made good ',

and proved bad ; the Master pushes her way out of it, through a screen of branches and briars, over a stony fence, flops into bog, struggles out, ascends to a commanding point of rock (in the eye of the wind and the teeth of the sleet) and begins to blow her Hounds out of covert. She thinks yearningly of her letters, her arm-chair, her fire, of, in short—'Home ! The woman's place ! ' But, as she says to herself, she promised the Cooladreen people to draw round the lake there, and there was talk of poisoning the foxes if they were neglected—and there was that awful hill, Drumlicky, she supposes she is bound to go on there, too, even though she knows only too well that there isn't 'a grain o' scent', nor the ghost of a fox above ground.

Poor Deputy Masters, who had, added to their other trials, the certainty that not a few among the non-subscribers to the Hunt had encouraged themselves in that particular war economy with the assertion that ' the hunting-field is *not* the Woman's Place ' !

I am far from trying to imply that the Deputy was unhappy. Far otherwise ; I believe she would tell you that her toil had its own compensations. I am also inclined to think that for those absent lads, whose bodies were in khaki in far-away places, while their hearts followed their well-beloved Hounds through the well-remembered home country, the place of those women who abandoned ' their proper place ', and went to the Kennels (if not to the dogs) to keep the hunts alive till the boys came home again, has not been so very far behind that high place of those other women whose more splendid part it was to seek and find the woman's place wherever their country needed their help, or suffering called for service.

X

A FOXHUNT IN THE SOUTHERN HILLS

THAT the seventeenth day of March should be established as the birthday of Ireland's chief Saint is of the nature of a compromise.

There is an old song, with an old tune, artless as it is consciously roguish, that expounds the position—

> *On the eighth day of March*
> *(Or so some people say)*
> *Saint Patrick at midnight,*
> *He first saw the day.*
> *But others declare*
> *'Twas the ninth he was born,*
> *So 'twas all a mistake*
> *Betwixt midnight and morn!*

The song, however, goes on to say that Father Mulcahy ('who showed them their sins'), having assured his flock that 'no one could have two birthdays, barrin' a twins', suggested that they should not be 'always dividin'', but should 'sometimes combine. Combine eight with nine, sivinteen is the mark—

Let that be his birthday !
Amin ! says the clerk.'

In spite, however, of Father Mulcahy's ingenious compromise, the celebrants of St. Patrick's Day have not often failed to find an excuse for breaking a head or two in his honour. Head-breaking reasons are still as plenty as ever in Ireland, and ' risings ' are prophesied as confidently by political prophets as are ' depressions from the south-west with wind and much rain ' by those who allot to us our daily share of the weather.

Nevertheless, one speaks of the ford as one finds it, and there still remain far-away places of Southern Ireland where tranquillity broods, and friendliness to all and sundry, and above all, friendliness to foxhunters and foxhounds, is firm and flourishing.

Yet it may confidently be asserted of one such place that a country less fitted by Providence for foxhunting would be far to find. A landscape must be pictured wherein little lakes and stretches of tawny bog fill all the level places, and, where these are not, the rest of the world is hill-side, grey with rock, dark with furze and heather. Squeezed in among the rocks are the white cottages, with a crooked ash-tree and a willow or two, between them and the south-west gales, each with its weedy patch of potatoes, and its enforced portion of tillage, drawn up about its knees like a brown blanket.

It was at a harsh and hideous National School (adjectives that are unhappily appropriate to most Irish National Schools) that the long hack, fifteen miles from Kennels, came to an end, and, as Hounds and Huntsman halted under its whitewashed walls, the war-time field, the few faithful women and farmers who had followed the Hunt into the wilderness, might have been justified in thinking that the 'rising', so often foretold, had at length taken place.

Suddenly and incredibly the bare and quiet country became alive. Not a ridge of hill but had its black fringe of figures, hardly a fence but a lad or two was slipping over it as lithely as a fox. The boys of two parishes were afoot, and there was not a self-respecting young man among them but had 'risen' to join the Hunt.

It was a mild and beaming day, with spring fluting in the larks' throats, and dancing in the wind that set the catkins on the willows tossing like little green lambs' tails. The furze-bushes were heaped with gold, and drenched with a scent as of apricots; the grass of the tiny pasture-fields was green as the most translucent jade (which has a hue incomparably fairer and sweeter than an emerald can show). At the end of a long valley of bog the mountains were azure and mauve; the nearer hills went through wallflower tones of bronze and brown to orange, where the dead bracken held the sunlight, or palest topaz, in the sedge that spread upwards from the low ground into the ravines through which the streams ran down to the bogs. Along the wall of the schoolhouse yard went a dazzling frieze of children's faces ; lovely faces, some of them, with the wonderful hair and eyes, and the glowing cheeks, that are bred of the soft breezes of these southern hills. Nothing save the clattering twitter of a flock of starlings could compare with the sound that ceaselessly proceeded from the frieze ; only the children themselves could sever a syllable from that torrent of swift speech. The schoolmaster, a tall and portly person, with a moustache like the mane of a chestnut horse, was one of the leading sportsmen, and had indeed invited the Hunt to the hills. In scarcely less mellifluous terms he now explained the ' most probable resort of the foxes ', and having rounded his last period, he delivered the visitors into the hands of one whom he described as ' a competent local Sisserone '. The Sisserone, a black-bearded farmer, stout and middle-aged, yet of tireless activity, affably accepted the Hunt as a composite godchild, and took on sole responsibility with alacrity.

'We'll bate the bog below,' he announced, ' and if the game isn't there we'll make for the mountain ! '

It was an impressive programme. Either the bog or the mountain might have seemed a sufficiently serious propo-sition, but Mikey-Dan (which is neither Japanese nor

Russian, and is merely the hyphenated title by which the middle-aged farmer was made known to his godchildren) had no shade of hesitation in his decisions. Without further preamble he lowered himself down a steep drop out of the road into a boggy field.

'Bring on the dogs!' he ordered briefly.

'Huic over!' said the Huntsman, with an equal brevity, and the Hounds flowed over the lip of the road, like water out of a basin, and followed Mikey-Dan.

So also did the few riders and the many runners. Born in the blood of the Irish country boy is the love of a horse. Hounds to him are no more than dogs, things of small account with which one turns cattle; mean creatures, to be treated meanly. But the horse, and especially the 'hunting-horse', is a gentleman, and is revered as such. To see Hounds run, they might say, is good, and it is a pleasant thing to behold the death of a fox, but what are these to watching a big-jumped horse throw a lep! There once befell a blank day in the country now being treated of, and the master (who was riding a 'big-jumped' mare) deplored to a farmer friend the disappointment that the lack of sport must have caused. He had forgotten the many and bizarre obstacles that had occurred during the day's fruitless wanderings. Not so the friend.

'Arrah, what disappointment had they? No! But they were well pleased. Kitty filled their eye!'

The ' bateing for game ' involved a sufficiency of dramatic interest, even though the leading gentleman of the piece, ' Charles James ' himself, was not on in the first scene. The art of *camouflage* has been studied with remarkable success by the bogs of this district, and after one horse had gone down by the head, even to his ears, and another by the stern, so that nothing was left of him above ground but the makings of a hobby-horse, and this in spots that might have been selected as putting-greens, riders began to feel that to find a fox might impart a liveliness beyond what was desired. Presently there ensued a boundary-drain, deep and intimidating, that looked as if it had been dug out of wedding-cake and filled with treacle.

' Could we walk through it ? ' suggested some one.

' You could not,' replied Mikey-Dan, ' that'd shwally the Kayser and all his min ! '

A war-time jest that was felt to be extremely smart and suitable for distinguished visitors.

The drain was not very wide, but it was wide enough, and what it economized in width it spent in depth. A place to gallop at, faintly trusting the larger hope that your horse will not refuse. But though the bog in which it is possible to gallop may exist in some favoured region, in Dereeny Bog it is not done—not, at least, by The Best People, who were undoubtedly those *intelligentsia* who unhesitatingly turned and hurried back, half a mile, to a bridge.

The Hounds made no delay, and pitched themselves across, with backs hooped like shrimps, the remaining horses, trembling (like their riders) in every limb, were half-coaxed, half-goaded into following them. One only, a cob ridden by a girl, failed to make a good landing, and the speed and skill with which the attendant cloud of witnesses pulled the girl off his back, and caught his head, and successfully aided his efforts, was memorable.

It was not long after the drain episode that Hounds found. They had quickened their pace after the crossing, and that unmistakable throb of purpose had come into their researches which, after a blank draw, lifts the Huntsman's heart. They spread themselves over the coarse sedge and rushes, and drew together with the eager sound that is more a whistle than a whimper, and then, just as hope was deepening to certainty, some watchers on the hill above the bog uttered those yells that, however habituated the hearer may be, have the quality that goes straight to the spinal marrow.

In an instant everything was running—Hounds, country boys, a spancelled donkey, a pair of coupled goats ; and the half-dozen riders, regardless of the practice of The Best People, were splashing and floundering across the bog after them. After the bog came a slope of rocks and furze, then a towering fence of stones and briars, unjumpable save at a 'gap' (attractively filled with long, thin slabs of stone, laid across it like the knives of a mowing-machine). A short struggle up and across the ' lazy-beds ' of a patch of potato-ground, and then the panting horses heaved themselves up a cattle-passage that resembled the shaft of a lift, and on to the road. And when they got there the Hounds and the country boys were gone as though they had never been.

A woman was knitting in the sun at a cottage door. She was a kind woman, and as the wild-eyed riders emerged, strenuously, from the lift, she arose and waved her knitting largely at the hill behind her little house.

' They're away up the mountain entirely ! ' she called to them.

The Huntsman, with a face already redder than his coat, drove his horse in a turkey-cock rush across the road and over the bank.

The hill-side rose sheerly above him. Little mellow flecks of sound came down, and told that the Hounds also were above him. There are not many things more hateful than fighting up a hill that is so steep that a rapidly extending view of the horse's backbone is presented to the rider, but when Hounds are out of sight many hateful things can happen unheeded, and a great deal can be done in five minutes, and, in rather less than that time, the Huntsman, and those few who clave to him, reached a level place—as it were a wider step in a stair-case—and made a pause. An appealing, questioning note on the horn was flung to the hill-top, and ' a voice replied, far up the height ', ' Hurry on ! They're this way ! '

. The mountain rose, in successive steps, sometimes heather and grass, more often bog, each step propped with a cliff of grey rock, and only to be gained by means of a connecting ravine.

The Huntsman, after the manner of his kind, was slipping ahead ; a despairing shout from one of his following caught him but just in time.

' Mike ! if ye see them, for God's sake give a roar to us ! '

Thus might Androcles have adjured his friendly lion.

A waft of Hounds' voices, sweeter at that moment than the songs of Paradise, came down the wind to the little striving company.

' Oh, get on ! get on ! ' says the girl on the cob, madly.

On the top of the mountain, a place that can best be likened to the carapace of a turtle, they caught the pack, checked for a moment, in the great wind that ever hurls over these high places. Mikey-Dan and a few of the elect were there also, watching with wary, narrowed eyes the opposite face of the nearest of the surrounding hills, whose rise and swell ceases only in that far-shining ocean which had suddenly leaped into view. The riders, arriving one by one, breathless, but happy again, received their praises proudly.

'THEY'RE AWAY UP THE MOUNTAIN ENTIRELY!'

' Ye proved good ! ye did, faith ! And the horses too ! It's a tough chase, but they'll have him yet ! '

And with the words the Hounds hit it once more, and were away over the shoulder of the hill through the heather, with a breast-high scent, and with a cry more tuneable than lark in any right-thinking shepherd's ear.

It was downhill this time, and the going was better. This side of the mountain had in some by-gone time been fenced, and a succession of stone walls of every type imparted an element of pleasing uncertainty. High single walls of lace-like open-work that toppled at a touch ; wide banks of small stones on which the horses changed feet with a crashing rattle ; upright spikes of rock with slanting spikes between, the interstices crammed with small stones ; the Southern Irish farmer plays tricks with his material with an infinite variation, and the Southern Irish horses jump his achievements with an infinite zest. It is hard to define wherein lies the peculiar delight of a hunt in the hills. In description it is the difficulties that fill the picture, but in the happy rider's mind it is the glories that remain, the times when Hounds are storming on the line, carrying a head like a flood in a river, and horses are pulling hard on the down grade, and no man living can predict the fox's point.

This particular fox steered a good course, and, crossing a grassy valley, bore away into moorland again. The runners, hardy though they were, had long since been beaten. The last heard of them was a shout from Mikey-Dan.

'It's into the say he's running, he's that much afraid o' ye.'

But Mikey-Dan was mistaken. In the middle of that desolate moor-country there stands a cliff that is like a tremendous door, closing an entrance to the heart of a hill. Old stories murmur about that mighty door, but what is behind it, a dead King, a Cluricaune's treasure, a Phuca, or a pathway to Fairyland, they do not dare to tell. The door is not a good fit; there is a space beneath it, hollowed out, one imagines, by the stream that flees from those hidden mysteries. The stories are afraid to tell us what they think is there, but in the minds of the Hounds there was no uncertainty. They told us that the fox was there, and they said it at the tops of their voices, and made no secret about it.

Printed in Great Britain by
Butler & Tanner Ltd.,
Frome and London